*Educational Statistics*

# Educational Statistics

## DONALD L. MEYER

*School of Education*
*Syracuse University*

The Center for Applied Research in Education, Inc.
*New York*

# *Foreword*

Dr. Meyer has made several wise decisions in the preparation of the present monograph on educational statistics. He has chosen to confine himself to a basic treatment of the rationale and procedure of statistical applications in education. He has avoided too great a coverage in view of available space resources. He has included, along with the more well known concepts, some unique topics and has drawn them together. Finally, he has kept in mind the fact that his monograph is a member, albeit an important one, of a series of monographs—the Library of Education Series—which is designed to be consumed by a certain class of reader.

The volume is devoted to the basics of probability, frequency and probability distributions and summarization of these distributions, estimation and hypothesis testing for the simple cases, the elements of Bayesian inference and a treatment of relationship and prediction. Dr. Meyer has presented contiguously the related descriptive and inferential aspects of statistical methodology. Many well chosen examples serve to illustrate and clarify the various content portions of the book.

As a result of the directness employed in the monograph, the reader can be expected to become minimally bogged down in onerous detail and be left to comprehend the overall fundamentals. Since the major purpose of the present volume is to fix fundamental concepts, it is noteworthy that the author has included a section on elementary Bayesian inference in educational settings and has connected these procedures to the so-called classical approach. Similarly, it is important to observe that since the volume has been written with the education community as its primary target, illustration and exposition closely follow this focus. Accordingly, Meyer's intimate acquaintanceship with the educative process and his involvement and interest in educational research cause his monograph and its message to become desirably palatable.

It is envisaged that the way in which the concepts of this volume have been sequenced and developed will aid in fostering the usefulness of statistical methodology in the contemplation and solution of educational problems. Consequently it is to be hoped that an educational practitioner or research worker will operate more knowledgeably upon digesting the contents of the volume. Just as it is true that in a monograph of the present length one cannot enter into the many complex situations which arise in educational settings, it is equally true that the foundations which should result from a study of the present volume will be invaluable in the understanding and appreciation of more complicated circumstances.

RAYMOND O. COLLIER

*Professor of Educational Psychology*
*University of Minnesota*

# Educational Statistics

## Donald L. Meyer

Dr. Meyer's *Educational Statistics* is, in many respects, a book which is basic to establishing an understanding of the other volumes in the Library of Education. A major use of statistics in the field of education involves ways of counting, recording, and reporting information in quantitative terms. Such results are needed in order to interpret reports and to understand implications relevant to school practice. In particular, the contents of this volume are especially necessary for an understanding of problems in evaluation and measurement and make a special contribution to understanding other volumes in the Series, such as *Testing Student Achievements and Aptitudes* by J. Stanley Ahmann and *Personal-Social Evaluation Techniques* by Merl E. Bonney and Richard S. Hampleman. Furthermore, since evaluation and measurement procedures generally lead to consideration being given to problems faced by counselors and other school personnel, a knowledge of statistics is essential to understanding those other volumes in the Library dealing with school psychology, guidance, counseling, special education, and those focused on pupil behavior. Finally, since so much of the contents of the entire Library is based on the results of research in diverse fields, it is worth pointing out that underlying this research are experimental procedures and designs utilizing the concepts described so well by Dr. Meyer.

Special efforts have been made by Dr. Meyer to select from the variety of definitions and concepts in the broad field of statistics those that have special relevance to the consumer in education who needs such background to interpret the literature in his own field. The author discusses definitions of statistics and their role in the field of education. He describes important statistical distributions and the basic characteristics of frequency distributions, including both measures of central tendency and variability. A very relevant problem in many fields of education is that of describing relationships. In a rigorous, straightforward fashion, Dr.

Meyer presents ways in which the statistician describes relationships and utilizes such relationships for prediction. Although it is difficult in a volume of this length to include the many important fields within statistics, Dr. Meyer has effectively presented a description of the problem of determining estimators by sampling procedures, and the concepts involved in utilizing statistical inference for testing hypotheses and setting up confidence intervals. As a unique feature, he comments on Bayesian inference and its effect on ways of utilizing statistics.

In addition to presenting, in a very readable and understandable fashion, basic vocabulary and concepts, Dr. Meyer has, throughout his volume, given numerical illustrations which will assist in conveying to the reader the types of usage and the application of the concepts to problems in typical school settings.

ERIC F. GARDNER
*Content Editor*

# *Contents*

# CHAPTER I

# Introduction

## What is Statistics?

The word, statistics, is ambiguous. It can refer to a set of data such as a collection of test scores. It can refer to various summary measures of data such as the mean or median, and it can refer to the field of study with which statisticians are concerned. If several statisticians are asked what it is they are concerned with, several different answers will likely be given. Such terms or phrases as "data analysis," "design of experiments," "random processes," "decisions under certainty," "quantitative methods," and the like will be forthcoming.

The lack of unanimity as regards the terms, "statistics" and "statistician" is due, in part, to the fact that statistics, as an independent discipline, is relatively new. The first "statisticians" were actually scientists in various fields, who developed and studied statistical methods, in order to describe data relevant to their investigations. The importance of this fact is: the motivation to develop statistics came from researchers who had various problems to solve in connection with their individual scientific work. When it was discovered that there were general statistical principles which could explain diverse phenomena, some researchers became interested in developing a theory of statistics. Chief among these men was R. A. Fisher, who probably did more to influence current statistical practice than any other person. The publication of his book, *Statistical Methods for Research Workers,*[1] in 1925, was a landmark event.

Today, partly due to the complexity of statistical theory, it is common to find statisticians who study the field of statistics as a discipline in itself. The primary justification of this study, however, is to aid scientists and others in describing and understanding various natural phenomena.

John Tukey, a leading American statistician and author of several statistical articles, has said:

---

[1] Fisher, Ronald A., *Statistical Methods for Research Workers,* 13th ed., (Edinburgh: Oliver and Boyd, Ltd., 1925, 1958).

1

All in all, I have come to feel that my central interest is in data analysis, which I take to include, among other things: procedures for analyzing data, techniques for interpreting the results of such procedures, ways of planning the gathering of data to make its analysis easier, more precise or accurate, and all the machinery and results of (mathematical) statistics which apply to analyzing data.[2]

Tukey does not equate "statistics" with data analysis, but the above statement is a succinct description of how many statisticians spend their time.

### The Role of Statistics in Education

In the field of education one of the major uses of statistics is that which the layman or non-professional usually thinks of when he hears the term "statistics." This involves what can be termed vital statistics or census type data. The number of students currently enrolled in a particular school system, and the number of school days attended in a particular school year are two examples of census type data. Obtaining answers to these two questions seems a fairly simple and straightforward task, but, in practice, certain difficulties immediately present themselves. How does one deal with the problem of transfer students during the school year? Should every student who attends school at least one day be counted or should some longer time period be used, say, three months? How about a school system located in an area having a large turn-over of industrial personnel, and, consequently, more than its share of transfer students? In such cases, wouldn't it be unfair to use too long a time period for crediting the school system with having a transfer student? Should absences be counted, and how? Before these questions can be answered, it must be determined why the data is being collected in the first place. If the answer is for curiosity only, certain simplifying procedures might be adopted. If, on the other hand, the data is to be presented to show the various categories of students and their respective times of attendance in order to determine how much state aid will be given to a school system, other procedures would have to be used. Unfortunately, some of these procedures are anything but simplifying!

Either way, some decisions have to be made so that intelligent use of the data can be made. These decisions consist of (1) adequately defining what is to be observed, (2) determining how the data is to be collected,

---

[2] Tukey, John W. in *Annals of Mathematical Statistics.* XXX, No. 1, March 1962, 3.

(3) how the results will be summarized, and (4) what use will be made of the results. Some of these decisions might not be considered to be within the domain of statistics, but rather, purely administrative. This holds true only insofar as the administrative decision is independent of the collection and analysis of the data. Some people hold the view that an administrator can call in his statistician and request "such and such" data be collected and analyzed, and that the use made of the results is solely the administrator's business. That this is a fallacious point-of-view can readily be determined if one examines the already mentioned "number of pupils enrolled." If the results gathered are to be used for some state-aid formula, the statistician must plan for the collection of the data to be sufficient to the precision required by the formula. He must attempt to define the study so that the results will be unbiased, in the sense that the data will accurately reflect the amount of state-aid which particular school systems should receive. Then, the results must be summarized in such a way that the formula can be applied.

It should not be concluded that all decisions are purely statistical. The administrator naturally is interested in how data will be collected, but, even though the statistician assures him that the proposed method is "correct" statistically, the cost involved might be greater than the problem warrants, and he will have to evaluate the worth of the project. For example, school personnel dramatically testify to the number of man-hours required in keeping attendance records. Multiplying this by the number of school districts in a state, adding in the machinery for reporting the results to the state department of education, it becomes evident that the cost of collecting this one "simple" statistic is large indeed. In oher words, the statistician must understand more than just the statistical aspects of the problem, and the user of the results (in this case, the administrator) must understand something about statistics.

Many examples of the census type can be found in the *NEA Research Bulletin* published by the National Education Association. A typical issue contains articles from "Small-Sample Techniques" through "Duty-Free Lunch Periods—A Break for Teacher" to "State-Local Taxes and You." Each of these articles reports statistical investigations.

Above, the discussion has focused on a large-scale type of investigation, but some of the same problems exist even down to the level of a single classroom teacher. Even here, adequate definitions, methods, etc. must still be considered. In addition, since the teacher might have only himself as a resource, the cost, perhaps in the form of teacher time, is an ever-present problem. As someone once said: "It's all relative, brother!"

At this point, it should be evident that statistics is not a science, but an art. There are some standard methods which are recognized to be effective, but the problems are so diverse and so unique that the statistician must be able to develop new or different techniques when the occasion arises. By re-reading Tukey's comments, in the light of the discussion on school attendance, one can appreciate how a statistician can be kept challenged by such an undertaking as *data analysis*.

A second use of statistics in education is in evaluation and measurement. Evaluation means the informal and formal assessments of students' performances, while measurement refers to the formal assessment of behaviors and constitutes part of evaluation. When the term, measurement, is used, it implies procedures utilizing pencil and paper tests, performance tests, and the like. Teachers make evaluations by observing everyday classroom behavior, by reading and grading assignments, by talking with students, etc. The teacher may utilize rating scales of various types which lead to the employment of statistical methods, but the principal uses made by teachers are in the sub-area of measurement. The most obvious use of statistics here is in the interpretation of test results. What can be done with individual scores and with groups of scores? How can results of classroom tests and stardardized tests be presented or combined in order to evaluate an individual student, a class, or a school system? A typical problem teachers face is the one of arriving at a single composite score for a student from two or three tests which had been given during the last grading period. The easiest solution—that of simply adding the two or three scores to obtain a single score—can be less than optimal in certain conditions. Statistics can lead to an understanding of these conditions and to offering a more acceptable solution.

The theory of mental testing, furthermore, involves considerable statistical thinking and methods. Concepts, such as reliability and validity, are precisely defined in terms of certain equations which are statistical in nature. The topic of item analysis and test item selection also requires statistics.

Evaluation and measurement procedures lead immediately to problems faced by counselors and other school personnel when they attempt to interpret past performances in order to predict future possibilities for individual students. The academic and/or vocational advice, which is given, is usually in the form of probabilities, not certainties, and, as such, relies heavily on statistical methods. Optimal methods of combining test scores with other types of information in order to improve prediction is an example of the use of statistics in this area.

A fourth use of statistics is in the area of researching into educational processes. Much research is empirically oriented and involves collection of data. The results are almost always statistical. The problem of how the study should be designed is crucial, in order that an unequivocal answer to the research problem be found. Unfortunately, theory and practice sometimes diverge and neat, clean answers are not always possible. Statistical methods can often focus one's thinking about these problems, and, at least, make clear what must be assumed by the research worker in order to arrive at a reasonable interpretation of the research results. Some statistical questions are: What variables are confounded? What is meant by subject-treatment interaction? What is the probability that the experimental effect is a chance effect?

There are other uses of statistics in education, but these are the principal ones. All of the issues raised above cannot be treated in one book or even in two or three. The remaining chapters of this book contain some of the statistical methods utilized in education and psychology; but more has been omitted than has been included. It is hoped that the reader will be motivated to follow-up, in more detail, topics which intrigue him and that this book will help him appreciate the fascination and potential of statistics.

# CHAPTER II

# Statistical Distributions

## Random Variables and Inductive Inference

The basic quantities that statisticians study are called variables. Most people are familiar with "mathematical" variables, but the variables dealt with in statistics are somewhat different. To emphasize this difference, they are called random variables. Before a definition of this term is given, some basis for understanding is needed.

Suppose it is contemplated to toss a six-sided die. This tossing is referred to as the fundamental experiment. Furthermore, the outcomes of this experiment are taken to be known. That is, before the die is tossed, it is possible to enumerate what might happen when the die is actually tossed. One of the numbers from one to six will appear on the upper face. Consequently, there are six possible outcomes of this experiment. Someone, at this time, always says, "This is fine, but what if the die should fall down a drain-pipe, or perhaps lodge against some object so that it stands on a corner and no number is face up?" One's answer to this is that these outcomes are declared to be inadmissible. For our purposes, the experiment never happened and the die would be thrown again. This explanation would satisfy theory, but, in practice, leads to difficulty. If the die fell down the drain-pipe, it might be impossible to throw it again! More about this later, but, for now, it is assumed all the outcomes are known.

The basis is: some fundamental experiment and a set of known outcomes. The next step is to assign a non-negative number to each of the outcomes such as the sum of all the numbers assigned is equal to one. These numbers are called the *probabilities* of the outcomes. Most people have an intuitive feeling about what probability means. Some people think of the probability of an outcome as the ratio of the number of times the outcome happens to the number of times the experiment is performed, provided the experiment is performed a large number of times. If a certain outcome has probability of one-half, it is true that, as the experiment is performed a million times, that the number of times the outcome would be observed would roughly be a half-million. Of course, it probably would not be a half-million exactly, but it would tend to be close to that figure. This type of definition leads to philosophical problems, such as how large is a "large number" of times, and it is virtually unusable for an outcome such as "this building will fall down." Some people think of probability as the degree of personal belief one feels. If one enters a particular building and conducts business there, one's personal probability that the building is unsafe must be fairly low. Others would rule out this type of outcome as a proper subject for probability. It is interesting to note that insurance companies, however, make it their business to deal with contingencies such as the collapsing of buildings. This question will not be pursued further here. The mathematical theory avoids this question by leaving probability as an undefined term.

It can be seen from the way probabilities are assigned that the smallest value of probability is zero and the largest is one. How are these probabilities assigned to the outcomes for our experiment? If it could be assumed that the die was fair in the sense of the outcomes being *equally likely,* then the total probability could be divided among the six outcomes equally resulting in each outcome having probability of $1/6$. Alternatively, it might be better not to make this assumption since the die could be biased. In this case some other values for the probabilities could be assigned or they could be left as unknown quantities, $p_2, p_1, \ldots, p_6$. A theory of probability could be developed by manipulating these quantities algebraically.

The basis is a fundamental experiment, a set of known outcomes and numbers, called probabilities, assigned to each of the outcomes. If a variable, X, is defined in terms of these outcomes, then the variable is called a *random variable.* Suppose X is defined as the number on the upper face of the die after the die is tossed. The possible values for this random variable are $1, 2, \ldots, 6$ and in the case of equally likely outcomes, the probability that X is less than or equal to the number one would be $1/6$. Similarly, the probability that $X \leq 2$ would be $2/6$ or $1/3$ (since the probabilities are additive). If the probabilities were assigned as $p_1, p_2, \ldots p_6$, then the corresponding probabilities would be $p_1$ for $X \leq 1$ and $p_1 + p_2$ for $X \leq 2$. A random variable differs from other types of variables in that the values for a random variable are *potential* values. In other terms, a random variable has a probability distribution.

Statisticians are interested in the probability distributions which exist for various random variables. In order to study these random variables and their distributions, surveys are taken, or experiments are performed, or other methods of data collection are used. If the random variable, X, defined above, were to be studied, the experiment of tossing the die could be performed. The die could be tossed several times, records could be kept of the number of times each face appeared, and estimates of the probabilities could be obtained by calculating various ratios.

Suppose the experiment were performed one-thousand times with the following results:

| Number on die | Observed frequency | Estimated probability |
|:---:|:---:|:---:|
| 6 | 804 | .804 |
| 5 | 42 | .042 |
| 4 | 54 | .054 |
| 3 | 62 | .062 |
| 2 | 38 | .038 |
| 1 | 0 | .000 |
| | 1000 | |

By dividing each observed frequency by one-thousand, the estimated probabilities are calculated as shown in the third column. It would appear that the assumption of equally likely faces is untenable, but it cannot be ruled out with absolute certainty. First, the relative frequencies obtained are only estimates. If the die were thrown several more times, the various ratios might each become closer to one-sixth. The tossing of the die might not have been a truly random tossing. That is, the die may have been held and then rolled in such a way that the number six would appear more frequently than it would have had the die been tossed in a different manner. This leads to another difficulty. What is meant by a "random" toss or a "good" toss? Practically speaking, it might be defined as the toss resulting from holding the die in a certain way, letting it fall from a certain height onto a smooth surface having a certain coefficient of elasticity, etc. In statistical terms, a random toss might be defined as a toss which results in a certain outcome, appearing with a probability equal to the true probability of the outcome. If you detect a circularity among these definitions, you are right. Can you appreciate, now, why mathematicians prefer to let the concept of probability be undefined?

What can be concluded from the experiment? The answer is that nothing can be concluded with absolute certainty, but some tentative conclusions can be drawn. First, if one feels confident that the tossing was done randomly, he might say that the die is not fair. He may be wrong when he makes this statement, but his "personal" probability of being wrong is thought to be low or very near zero.

So far, one conclusion has been stated. The die is not fair. A further conclusion could be made that the number six is most likely. This statement is not completely independent of the "non-fair" statement, but it does contain an additional assertion. Most people feel very confident that this statement is true, and one could attempt to assess one's "personal" probability or one's degree of belief in the conclusion.

A list of possible conclusions is summarized below:

A. The die is not fair.
B. Number six is most likely.
C. Number one is least likely.
D. Number three is the second most likely outcome.
E. Numbers three and four are equally likely.
F. Numbers two and five are equally likely.
G. Number one has probability equal to zero.
H. There is a weight in the die which causes the number one to tend to be face down.

The third statement, conclusion C, might not be as readily accepted as the first two. While the evidence is such that most people would not care to wager even money that a one would appear before a two appeared on future successive tosses of the die, it is also true that the evidence is not overwhelming. That is, if someone were willing to pay fifty dollars against your one dollar that a two would appear before the one, you just might take that bet. Conclusion C, however, does not only state that a one is less likely than a two, but also that a one is less likely than each of the other numbers. The wager might be that a one would appear before any of the other numbers. If conclusion B were accepted, the possible numbers which could be "least likely" are restricted to the numbers one to five. The difficulty in readily accepting conclusion C is that each of the numbers one to five are unlikely.

When conclusion D is considered, one feels even less confident that it is a true statement. The probability that this is only a random fluctuation and that number four, say, is actually more likely is higher than the analogous probabilities for conclusions A, B and C.

The data tends to support conclusions E and F. The estimated probabilities for numbers two and five are very close, and the difference between them could very possibly have been due to random fluctuations. If more tosses were effected, the estimated probabilities might become even closer. On the other hand, just the reverse could happen. That is, with more tosses, the estimated probabilities could diverge.

Conclusion G is of a different type from those preceding it. Each of the previous statements asserted something about the relationship among the probabilities of the various outcomes, but no particular value for any probability was stated. Conclusion G goes further and states one particular value for the probability of number one occurring. Certainly, this is a strong conclusion. Note that one could conclude that the estimated probability is the true probability of the outcome, but no one would be too surprised if the conclusion were false and the true probability were somewhat different from the estimated probability after one-thousand tosses. The true probability of a "one" occurring could be .005 or some other value near zero, and the observed frequency of zero occurrences of the number one would still be a consistent result.

Conclusion H is yet another type. This conclusion is extra-statistical, although it may have been suggested by statistical evidence. Since the numbers one and six are on opposite sides of the usual die, the frequent occurrence of the number six could be related to the infrequent occurrence of the number one through the mechanism of a type of weight or "load" in the die. This weight would tend to cause the die to come to rest with the number one face down. The occurrence of the other numbers could be explained by this same mechanism. If the weight were not too heavy or if it were positioned in the die in a certain way, then the particular velocity of the toss or the particular corner of the die which first came into contact with the surface upon which the die is rolled may cause the die to behave in an "imperfect" manner. The die would come to rest on an adjacent face to the number one face. Some experience with various loaded dice could help us to know if this were a reasonable explanation.

This is essentially how statistical arguments are developed. A desire or a need to study some process or phenomenon evolves. A random variable is defined, and data is collected pertaining to that variable. Using the mathematical theory of probability, which may involve some rather sophisticated calculations and manipulations, certain conclusions are made. These are held to be true or untrue, depending on the probabilities which are ascribed to them. These probabilities may be "personal" probabilities to the extent that they differ depending upon the individual.

This method of reasoning is characterized as being "inductive," since certain generalizations are drawn from particular instances. This is in contradistinction with mathematics which starts with a consideration of certain premises, and then after using a process of deduction arrives at logical implications, which must be true provided the premises and the method of reasoning have been correct. In tossing the die above, an attempt to make generalizations about the probabilities from an examination of one thousand particular tosses is made. Any conclusions so drawn could be incorrect, even if the experimental method were granted to be "correct" and if our reasoning were granted to be logical. In many instances of statistical investigations, the problem is very complex. The method of collecting data is often the first factor criticized, to say nothing of criticism made of research workers who often are called "liars, damned liars, and statisticians."

Most, or all, of our scientific "truths" have been arrived at by a process of induction, and it should be emphasized that they are true only in a probability sense. Will the sun rise tomorrow? Probably! Is the law of gravity true as Newton stated it? At one time scientists would have answered, "Probably." But, today, they might answer, "Probably not." One could characterize scientific thinking as that which allows for some probability—or that what is stated to be true is in fact not true.

Lawyers try to present their cases in such a way that their arguments appear plausible or credible to the jury. If in the minds of the jury the probability that the accused is guilty is sufficiently close to one, then a guilty verdict is voted. "Beyond the shadow of a doubt" does not mean certainty! A statistical argument which resulted in the dismissal of two students from college was one in which the author served as a consultant. A multiple-choice examination of one-hundred questions had been administered to a certain class. Two students sitting next to each other had been observed as "acting suspiciously." Their answer sheets (of the IBM type) were later examined by the professor. Not only did they get many of the same questions correct, but, on the items they answered incorrectly, they marked the same incorrect responses. The actual calculation of the probability that this would happen by chance is difficult to assess. First, the items themselves differed in difficulty. That is, some of the items were easy for the class, and some were quite difficult. If the test, as a whole, were easy, then it would be expected that many students would get the same questions correct. In general, if the *discriminating power* of the test were low, one would expect students to obtain the same total scores and even many of the same questions correct. Furthermore, an item analysis might reveal that the questions which were missed tended to be missed in just the way that the two students happened to have marked them. From a scrutiny of their responses, together with the class responses on the test items, it was decided that the probability that the observed results could have happened *assuming the students were marking their papers independently,* was very near zero. Consequently, it was concluded that the two students had been cheating, and they were reported to the dean of the college. The dean hoped that by confronting the students with the evidence a confession would be forthcoming, which is exactly what happened.

The example concerning the tossing of the die was illustrative of "after the fact" type arguments. The data was collected, examined, and then conclusions suggested by the data were drawn. One must be cautious when arguing in this manner, because there is a tendency to over-generalize from particular relationships found in a particular set of data. In fact, any series of random numbers contains several patterns which might first be thought of as indicative of a general relationship. With any finite series of numbers, a mathematician can find an algebraic expression which relates the particular numbers with their position in the series. The test, of course, is whether this relationship would continue to hold when more numbers were generated. The same thing is true of the conclusions drawn from the data on the tossing of the die. The conclusions might better be thought of as hypotheses which can be tested by further experimentation.

Researchers, oftentimes, develop a probability model for a certain process or mechanism, based on existing theory and previous experimentation. They test the model by making certain derived predictions and then collecting relevant data which either tends to prove or dis-prove their assertations. By a constant interplay of theory and data, new models are formulated or old ones revised. Two examples of this type of endeavor are genetics and statistical learning theory.

The practical application of theory is not as precise as one would like to have it. In discussing outcomes of an experiment, it is assumed these are known. It is easy, in theory, to declare something like the die rolling down a pipe as being inadmissable. In practice, however, this type of outcome does happen and is not easily dismissed. In a T-maze experiment with rats, the random variable under study might be the right or left turning of a rat at the T after a certain training period. What does one do if the rat refuses to move down the alley-way? What does one do if the rat dies? In educational studies a student might become ill during a critical phase of the study and, thereby, receive some special attention which hadn't been planned for. In a reading experiment, a student is sometimes given the wrong test booklet and responds to the wrong question. Many times, dying rats or ill students are omitted from the study.

Such deviations limit the generalizability of a study, and it is difficult, if not impossible, to include them when making a formal analysis of the data. Such are the challenges of scientific investigation.

## The Frequency Distribution

The study of random variables usually results in a frequency distribution of observations. This is nothing more than a systematic arrangement of the observed frequencies of the various values of the studied variable. Table 1 shows the frequency distribution resulting from a quiz given to an elementary statistics class.

TABLE 1

FREQUENCY DISTRIBUTION OF TEST SCORES

| Test score(X) | frequency(f) |
|---|---|
| 29 | 1 |
| 28 | 2 |
| 27 | 2 |
| 26 | 4 |
| 25 | 1 |
| 24 | 2 |
| 23 | 2 |
| 22 | 7 |
| 21 | 2 |
| 20 | 5 |
| 19 | 8 |
| 18 | 4 |
| 17 | 5 |
| 16 | 5 |
| 15 | 3 |
| 14 | 2 |
| 13 | 2 |
| 12 | 2 |
| 11 | 1 |
| 10 | 5 |
| 9 | 3 |
| 8 | 2 |
| 7 | 3 |
| 6 | 1 |
| 5 | 0 |
| 4 | 1 |
| 3 | 0 |
| 2 | 1 |
| | 76 |

The seventy-five student's test scores have been grouped in the most elementary manner. Rather than writing each individual's score separately, identical scores have been grouped together. Some facts are immediately evident. First, the highest and lowest scores are 29 and 2 respectively. Second, the scores are less dense at the lower end of the distribution than they are at the upper end, which illustrates why it is good practice to show all the scores within the score range, even if they have zero frequencies. Third, the most frequently occurring scores are 19 and 22, which are closer to the high end of the distribution than the lower end. In this manner, one could continue summarizing the information shown by the frequency distribution. What the data is to be used for dictates what information is to be noted. If a teacher wants to use the distribution as a basis for giving final grades, no further summarization is necessary, except, perhaps, the calculation of percentage frequencies, if the teacher gives grades according to some standard percentages. If the test results are to be communicated to someone else, it might be desirable to summarize the data further in the interest of parsimony. If this set of data were to be compared with another set of like data, other techniques could be used. The important point is: the statistical techniques to be applied depends upon the particular purposes one has in mind. Several statistical methods are presented below and throughout this book, but it is not implied that all or any part of them are relevant to every problem.

Sometimes patterns become more obvious if the data are grouped further. Table 2 shows the same frequency distribution of test scores, but this time grouped in score intervals of various sizes. These intervals are referred to as class intervals. There are no rules for constructing the intervals relative to either their size or the placement of the intervals as

TABLE 2

FREQUENCY DISTRIBUTION OF TEST SCORES: INTERVALS OF VARIOUS SIZES

| size 2 | | size 3 | | size 4 | |
|---|---|---|---|---|---|
| x | f | x | f | x | f |
| 28–29 | 3 | 29–31 | 1 | 26–29 | 9 |
| 26–27 | 6 | 26–28 | 8 | 22–25 | 12 |
| 24–25 | 3 | 23–25 | 5 | 18–21 | 19 |
| 22–23 | 9 | 20–22 | 14 | 14–17 | 15 |
| 20–21 | 7 | 17–19 | 17 | 10–13 | 10 |
| 18–19 | 12 | 14–16 | 10 | 6–9 | 9 |
| 16–17 | 10 | 11–13 | 5 | 2–5 | 2 |
| 14–15 | 5 | 8–10 | 10 | | 76 |
| 12–13 | 4 | 5–7 | 4 | | |
| 10–11 | 6 | 2–4 | 2 | | |
| 8–9 | 5 | | 76 | | |
| 6–7 | 4 | | | | |
| 4–5 | 1 | | | | |
| 2–3 | 1 | | | | |
| | 76 | | | | |

regards the top and bottom score. For intervals of size two the lowest score of 2 is the lower apparent limit of the bottom class interval, while the highest score of 29 is the upper apparent limit of the top interval. (A word about the use of the "apparent" later.) For intervals of size three this placing of the lowest and highest score is impossible, which is also true for intervals of size four. This is one instance of a general fact that grouping of data usually results in some loss of information. The individual test scores are unknown to a person who sees only the grouped data. If this loss of information is serious, one doesn't group. Again, the uses one wishes to make of the data would dictate the procedure used. Some writers recommend that less than fifty scores should never be grouped. Some recommend that no fewer than twenty class intervals be used while others say ten or fifteen. Blanket statements of this type are helpful only to the extent that readers are made aware of the consequences of grouping data.

An interesting fact is somewhat more apparent when intervals of size two are employed. Instead of the frequencies steadily decreasing at both ends of the distribution from the high of ten and twelve frequencies between 16 and 19, the frequencies first decrease, then increase, and at the very ends decrease again. This is even more striking if intervals of size three are used. Towards both ends the frequencies dip to five, then increase to eight and ten at the upper and lower ends respectively with a subsequent decrease further towards the two ends. This can be seen in Figures 1 and 2 which are *frequency polygon* graphs of the two distributions.

The horizontal axis serves as the scale for the variable X, test score, while the vertical axis is the scale of observed frequencies. The frequencies are plotted against the mid-points of the respective class intervals. In figure 1, frequencies of 1, 1, 4, . . . are plotted against the mid-points, 2.5, 4.5, 6.5, . . . while in figure 2, the frequencies 2, 4, 10, . . . are plotted against the mid-points, 3, 6, 9, . . . . . Two additional points are

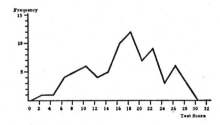

Figure 1. Frequency Polygon: Intervals of Size Two

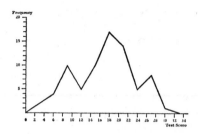

Figure 2. Frequency Polygon: Intervals of Size Three

plotted as zero frequencies for the next highest and lowest mid-points. In figure 1, these mid-points are .5 and 30.5, while, in figure 2, these mid-points are 0 and 33. All the points are then connected by straight lines.

The score value which occurs most frequently is called the *mode*. For intervals of size two the mode would be declared as 18.5, the mid-point of the interval with the most frequencies. For intervals of size three, the mode would be reported as 18. If there are other values, which have relatively high scores as compared with adjacent scores, these values are sometimes referred to as relative modes. The distribution is called unimodal, bimodal, etc., depending upon the number of relative modes. The graph for intervals of size two is quite saw-toothed but shows a relative mode near the high end of the distribution, while the graph for intervals of size three seems to be trimodal. This is a case in point where an interesting pattern can be observed which may well disappear with a larger sample size or which is the result of random measurement error on the test. If one makes too much of this observed result, he may be guilty of over-generalization.

The author has very often observed at least bimodal distributions on statistics and mathematics examinations. An explanation for this is: if many of the test items hinge upon one or two principles taught in class, a student who grasps these principles will get most of the relevant items correct, while the opposite is true of the student who does not understand the principles. This tends to cause the distribution to be bimodal. However, this appears not to be the case on this test. Wait, though! If this is not the case, and bimodal distributions are usually observed, what has happened? This particular test consisted of two parts completely different in content. The first part was of the multiple choice type, which supposedly measured "understanding" of statistics, and the second part consisted of problems requiring computational skills, which could be learned mechanically. Suppose the two parts were scored separately. Perhaps the

16

bimodality effect would be more obvious . . . and suppose . . . and suppose. . . . This type of statistical detective work can be fun, but, as pointed out previously, can also be dangerous, if sweeping generalizations are made from limited data.

The frequency distribution grouped into intervals of size four appears to be unimodal and fairly regular. (See Figure 3.) This usually happens as the size of the intervals increase. The distribution could continue to be grouped into wider and wider intervals, until all detail becomes lost and one has grouped himself right out of business!

The variable, test score, is said to be *discontinuous* or *discrete* since there are gaps in the range of potential values for X. It is impossible for a value such as 18.3 to be observed, since the basic unit of measurement is one score point for each correct item. However, a little reflection will show that all measurements are discrete. No matter how precisely a measurement is taken, the measurement is always rounded off. If the length of an object is to be measured, some very precise instrument may be used, but the measurement is only to the nearest ten-thousandth of an inch or one-millionth of an inch etc. The variable, length, is thought of as being continuous, because any length in a certain range is possible. Anybody who is more than five feet tall had to be at one time in their life exactly 4.6704320021468 . . . etc. feet. Such is the nature of a continuous variable. The variable may be continuous, but the measurement is discontinuous. Consequently, if length is being measured to the nearest inch, a reported measurement of 7 inches could be any length from 6.5 to 7.5 inches. If the length were greater than 7.5 inches, the measurement would be rounded to 8 inches. Similarly, if the measurements were taken to the nearest one-tenth of an inch, a reported measurement of 4.3 inches would be interpreted as 4.25 to 4.35 inches. Sometimes, measurements are rounded to the last whole unit. When a person reports his age as 24, he means he is at least 24, but not greater than 24.9999 . . . years, or 25.

A test score of 18 is interpreted as a measurement on a continuous variable achievement. Consequently, 18 represents 17.5 to 18.5. The test score of 18 could also be interpreted as being rounded to the last unit so that 18 would represent a measurement in the interval 18 to 18.999. . . . The first interpretation, 17.5 to 18.5, is conventionally used, however.

Referring to the frequency distribution grouped into intervals of size two, the bottom interval is reported as 2–3. The *exact* class limits are

1.5 and 3.5. The exact class limits for the next interval are 3.5 and 5.5. Similarly, for intervals of size three, the exact class limits for the top interval are 28.5 and 31.5. If one subtracts the lower exact limit of any class interval from the upper exact limit of the same interval, the length of the interval is determined. For example, 31.5 minus 28.5 equals 3, while 5.5 minus 3.5 equals 2. This is not true of the apparent class limits, which are the integral values shown in Table 3, (i.e. 31 minus 29 equals 2, but the interval size is 3).

The histogram is another graphical device used to illustrate a frequency distribution. Instead of using height to represent frequencies, the graphical unit is area. Bars are erected over each class interval showing that the total area of each bar is proportional to the number of frequencies in each interval. The area of a bar is equal to the length of the class interval multiplied by the height of the bar. Therefore, if the class intervals are equal in length, as they were for the test score distributions, then the area of each bar is a function of only the height of the bar. The histogram for the test score distribution with intervals of size four is shown in Figure 3. Note that the bars are drawn to exact class limits. If the mid-

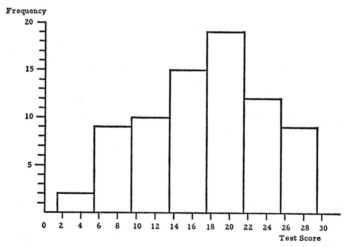

Figure 3. Histogram: Intervals of Size Four

points of the bars are connected by straight lines, then the frequency polygon is formed.

Since area is the graphing unit, the histogram may be drawn for frequency distributions which have been grouped into unequal class intervals. One of the purposes of grouping is to reduce the data to a manageable size so that the principal features or patterns will be obvious to users of the data. If equal class intervals are used to group data, which has a large range, then, oftentimes, many of these intervals will have few or no cases, while some of the intervals will have a large number of cases. The distribution of towns and cities by population size is such an example. In New York state the largest city is New York City with roughly 8,000,000 population; the smallest town is, roughly, 100 or effectively zero. If twenty class intervals were used, each class interval would be 400,000 in length. All of the towns and cities would be grouped in one interval, except for two cities. There would be many intervals with no frequencies. Suppose New York City is dropped from the distribution, with the intention of reporting it separately. The next most populated cities in New York State are: Buffalo 532,759; Rochester 318,611; Syracuse 216,038; Albany 129,726. Using Buffalo as the largest city, the twenty equal class intervals would each be approximately of length 26,600. Again, we would find over ninety percent of the towns and cities in two intervals. If Buffalo is dropped and Rochester used as the largest city, intervals of approximately 16,000 would again result in over ninety percent of the towns and cities in two or three intervals. Even if Albany is used as the largest city, ninety percent would fall into less than ten intervals. This procedure of dropping cities becomes ridiculous, of course. Either more class intervals must be used—which is not in the spirit of reducing our data to a manageable size—or detail must be sacrificed. One solution is to use unequal class intervals. In some parts of the distribution, intervals of 1000 in length might be used, while in other parts, intervals of 300,000 could be used. Detail would be retained for the majority of towns, while the interesting feature of population distribution in New York state could still be exhibited.

An example of a milder distribution of this type is given in Table 3. The bottom and top intervals, as reported in the original research article, are already unequal intervals. The bottom interval can be taken as 1–15, but it is not obvious what should be done with the top interval. The highest class size could be 75, 80, or 100. The next three lower intervals have densities of .006, .003, and .007 percent, which is an average of about .005 percent. If each of the class sizes from 56 on up had densities of .005 percent, thirteen intervals of size one would be needed (i.e. .065 ÷ .005 equals 13). Therefore, the upper interval would be 56–68. This is only an approximation, as the assumption of equal density of .005 is probably

TABLE 3

ESTIMATED NUMBER AND PERCENT OF URBAN ELEMENTARY-SCHOOL
CLASSES BY SIZE, NOVEMBER, 1959
*Source:* NEA Research Bulletin, Vol. 38, Oct. 1960

| Number of pupils per class | Number of classes | Percent of total |
|---|---|---|
| 56 or more | 290 | .065 |
| 55 | 27 | .006 |
| 54 | 13 | .003 |
| 53 | 33 | .007 |
| 52 | 50 | .012 |
| 51 | 46 | .010 |
| 50 | 64 | .014 |
| 49 | 67 | .015 |
| 48 | 221 | .050 |
| 47 | 272 | .061 |
| 46 | 357 | .080 |
| 45 | 539 | .121 |
| 44 | 864 | .194 |
| 43 | 1,279 | .287 |
| 42 | 1,922 | .431 |
| 41 | 2,707 | .608 |
| 40 | 4,491 | 1.008 |
| 39 | 6,214 | 1.394 |
| 38 | 9,007 | 2.022 |
| 37 | 12,005 | 2.694 |
| 36 | 15,908 | 3.570 |
| 35 | 20,750 | 4.656 |
| 34 | 24,472 | 5.492 |
| 33 | 27,236 | 6.112 |
| 32 | 30,978 | 6.952 |
| 31 | 33,035 | 7.414 |
| 30 | 36,196 | 8.123 |
| 29 | 32,458 | 7.284 |
| 28 | 31,819 | 7.141 |
| 27 | 28,049 | 6.295 |
| 26 | 25,361 | 5.691 |
| 25 | 23,030 | 5.168 |
| 24 | 18,408 | 4.131 |
| 23 | 14,759 | 3.312 |
| 22 | 11,287 | 2.533 |
| 21 | 8,649 | 1.941 |
| 20 | 7,114 | 1.597 |
| 19 | 4,320 | .969 |
| 18 | 3,414 | .767 |
| 17 | 1,968 | .441 |
| 16 | 1,434 | .322 |
| 15 or fewer | 4,487 | 1.007 |
| *Total* | 445,600 | 100.00 |

not true. It is a simplifying assumption, however, and the error made in using it is not likely to be bothersome for most applications.

As it stands, there are forty-two intervals of which forty are of size one, one of size thirteen, and one of size fifteen. A histogram could be constructed now, but suppose it is desired to further reduce the data to about fifteen intervals. There are many alternative ways of further grouping the data, the particular choice depending on the amount and kind of detail desired. In Table 4 the data have been grouped into sixteen intervals in such a way that no class size containing five percent or larger of the total number of classes has been grouped with another class size. Furthermore, some detail has been retained in the "tails" of the distribution. The 1–15 interval has not been further grouped, and no class size containing more than five times the frequency in another class size has been grouped with that class.

TABLE 4

DATA OF TABLE 3 GROUPED INTO UNEQUAL CLASS INTERVALS

| Number of pupils per class | Number of classes | Percent of Total |
|---|---|---|
| 44–68 | 2,843 | .638 |
| 39–43 | 16,613 | 3.728 |
| 35–38 | 57,670 | 12.942 |
| 34 | 24,472 | 5.492 |
| 33 | 27,236 | 6.112 |
| 32 | 30,978 | 6.952 |
| 31 | 33,035 | 7.414 |
| 30 | 36,196 | 8.123 |
| 29 | 32,458 | 7.284 |
| 28 | 31,819 | 7.141 |
| 27 | 28,049 | 6.295 |
| 26 | 25,361 | 5.691 |
| 25 | 23,030 | 5.168 |
| 21–24 | 53,103 | 11.917 |
| 16–20 | 18,250 | 4.096 |
| 1–15 | 4,487 | 1.007 |
| Total | 445,600 | 100.000 |

The histogram for the resulting distribution is shown in Figure 4. The horizontal axis is the scale of the variable, class size, and, the vertical axis is percentage frequency per unit class size. (Percentages have been used merely for convenience.) The first task in constructing a histogram of this sort is to choose a unit of area. The simplest choice is to let a rectangle one unit of width on the horizontal scale by one unit of height

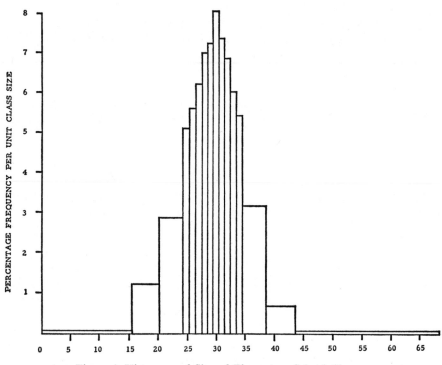

Figure 4. Histogram of Size of Elementary School Classes

on the vertical scale equal one percent of the total frequency. The height of the bars, corresponding to each of the class intervals 25 through 34, will be simply the percentage frequency in the interval, since these class intervals are each of size one. The height of the bar for the interval 1–15 is computed as follows:

A. The length of the interval is computed to be 15.5 minus .5 equal to 15.
B. Since the total area must equal 1.007 percent, the height of the bar is 1.007 ÷ 15 equal to .067.

Similarly, since the length of the next interval is 20.5 minus 15.5 equal to 5, the height of the next bar is 4.096 ÷ 5 equal to .819.

Inspection of the percentage frequencies in Table 4 might lead one to conclude that the modal value occurs in the class interval, 35–38, since 12.942 is the largest percentage frequency listed. It must be remembered, however, that unequal class intervals have been used, and that the percentage, 12.942, is spread over four class sizes (i.e. 38.5–34.5 = 4).

Consequently, the "average" percentage for this interval is 12.942 ÷ 4 or 3.235. This is the height of the bar for this interval in Figure 4.

A prominent feature of the histogram, for elementary school classes, is the large variability among the class sizes. This is seen from the long tails on both ends of the graph, and the fact that the modal class size of 30 contains only 8.1% of the total number of classes. In addition 34%, or about one-third of the total number of classes, is of size 24 and smaller, or 35 and larger. The histogram, using unequal intervals, adequately displays this variability while retaining a maximum amount of detail.

It is convenient to classify frequency distributions by the various types of "smooth" curves, which connect the mid-points of the bars of the histograms. Figure 5 shows a variety of curves, which apply to various distributions found in practice. Curves c and d are typified by a short range of the variable, X, having relatively high density and a long range of relatively low density. The difference between them is the position of

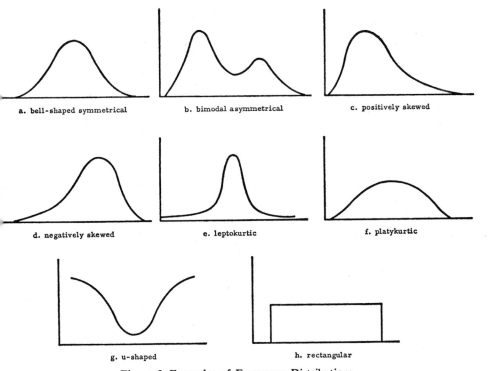

a. bell-shaped symmetrical    b. bimodal asymmetrical    c. positively skewed

d. negatively skewed    e. leptokurtic    f. platykurtic

g. u-shaped    h. rectangular

Figure 5. Examples of Frequency Distributions

the "tail" and "hump." An easy way to remember the correct labelling is to recall that "to skew" means to distort or change. The long tail is a distortion from symmetry. Hence, if the tail is to the right or in the positive direction on the axis, the curve is positively skewed. If the long tail is to the left, then the curve is negatively skewed. The characteristics of a leptokurtic curve (e) are long tails and tall hump. The platykurtic curve (f) is characterized by a short hump and relatively short tails.

# CHAPTER III

# The Summarization of Information

## Central Values

In the preceding section, the distribution of elementary school class sizes was considered. This data was presented graphically and was summarized by noting that the distribution had long tails and a mode of 30. These two descriptions were used to communicate some of the information contained in the distribution. It is an economical description in the sense that one number and one phrase summarizes 445,600 observations on class size. Various statistical quantities can be calculated from a frequency distribution, each one of them summarizing some of the information contained in the data. If these quantities describe features of the distribution which are relevant to a particular problem, then, in addition to economy, they can serve to focus attention.

The statistics to be discussed in this section are the so-called "measures of central tendency" or "measures of location." These include the arithmetic mean, median, mode, and mid-range. The motivation for such a measure: to summarize, in a single number, the location of the frequency distribution on the scale of the variable, $X$. When the mode of 30 is reported for the distribution of class sizes, the distribution is "pinned down" on the scale of $X$. Other quantities could be calculated to locate a distribution. The largest class size, for example, communicates some information concerning location; however, a more central value, about which the distribution varies, is preferred.

The *mid-range* is the value on the scale of the random variable, $X$, which is half-way between the highest and lowest values occurring in the sample. Referring to Table 2, the mid-range for the distribution of test scores is calculated as follows:

  a. The range is $29-2 = 27$
  b. Half the range is 13.5
  c. The mid-range is $2 + 13.5 = 15.5$

Calculation of the mid-range for grouped data requires some assumption. The distribution of test scores grouped into intervals of size three is reproduced in Table 5, together with three additional columns which will be explained below. Inspection of the two extreme intervals does not

TABLE 5

DISTRIBUTION OF TEST SCORES: INTERVALS OF SIZE THREE

| X | f | mid-points (X) | fX | fX$^2$ |
|---|---|---|---|---|
| 29–31 | 1 | 30 | 30 | 900 |
| 26–28 | 8 | 27 | 216 | 5832 |
| 23–25 | 5 | 24 | 120 | 2880 |
| 20–22 | 14 | 21 | 294 | 6174 |
| 17–19 | 17 | 18 | 306 | 5508 |
| 14–16 | 10 | 15 | 150 | 2250 |
| 11–13 | 5 | 12 | 60 | 720 |
| 8–10 | 10 | 9 | 90 | 810 |
| 5–7 | 4 | 6 | 24 | 144 |
| 2–4 | 2 | 3 | 6 | 18 |
|  | N = 76 | 165 | 1296 | 25236 |

give certain knowledge regarding the extreme scores. The assumption usually made is that the mid-point of the interval will adequately represent the scores within the interval. The mid-points of each of the intervals are shown in the third column. Using this assumption, the mid-range is calculated as follows:

    a. Range is 30–3 = 27
    b. Half the range is 13.5
    c. Mid-range is 3 + 13.5 = 16.5

Note that this value does not agree with that calculated from the ungrouped distribution. This is a practical interpretation of the phrase "loss of information from grouping."

The mid-range is a "middle" type value, but it does not utilize any information regarding the actual distribution of scores within the given range. If the score values within the given range were simply averaged, then the result would be the mid-range. For the ungrouped distribution in Table 2, one would add the score values which gives 434, and divide by their number, 28. This yields 15.5 which agrees with that found previously. In Table 5 the mid-points are being used to represent the scores in an interval. These mid-points would be added (165) and divided by their number (10)—yielding 16.5 which again agrees. The mid-range, therefore, is an average, but the actual distribution of frequencies is disregarded.

One way of using the frequencies would be to calculate a weighted average of the score values. The weights would be given by the frequencies with which each score value occurs. In Table 5, each mid-point has been weighted by (or multiplied by) the frequencies. The results are shown in the fourth column. Adding this column, and, then, dividing by the sum of the weights gives 1296/76, or 17.1. This quantity is called the *arithmetic mean,* or simply, mean. (The fifth column should be disregarded at this time.) Note that the mean is larger than the mid-range in this example. This occurs because the weights in the upper half of the distribution are larger than those in the lower half.

The mean, then, is defined to be the weighted average of the score values of the variable, x, where the weights are given by the frequencies with which each score value occurs. This definition can be summarized in algebraic notation. Let $x_1$ be the lowest value of x and $f_1$ be the corresponding frequency of $x_1$. Let $x_2$ be the next highest value of x and $f_2$ its frequency, etc., to $x_k$, the highest value with $f_k$ its frequency. Then

$$\text{mean} = \frac{f_1 x_1 + f_2 x_2 + \ldots + f_k x_k}{f_1 + f_2 + \ldots + f_k}$$

The summation process can be shown in a shorter manner by defining a summation sign or operator. Let the Greek letter "sigma," $\Sigma$, represent summation. Then we could write

$$\text{mean} = \frac{\Sigma f_i x_i}{\Sigma f_i} \quad (i = 1, 2, \ldots k)$$

where the subscript, i, is merely an index of summation, showing that the summation takes place as "i" takes on successive values, 1, 2, . . . k.

The symbol, $\overline{X}$, read "x-bar," is usually used to represent the mean, and because $\Sigma f_i$ is the sum of the frequencies, N, the mean can be written as $\overline{X} = \frac{\Sigma f_i x_i}{N}$.

The mean for the ungrouped distribution would be calculated in the same manner, i.e. $(1)(2) + (0)(3) + (1)(4) + \ldots + (2)(27) + (2)(28) + (1)(29)$ divided by 76. The resulting calculation is shown below, together with the means, modes, and mid-ranges for the other groupings of the test score distributions shown in Table 2.

|  | *Mean* | *Mid-range* | *Mode* |
|---|---|---|---|
| Ungrouped (Table 1) | 17.2 | 15.5 | 19.0 |
| Intervals of size two | 17.3 | 15.5 | 18.5 |
| Intervals of size three | 17.1 | 16.5 | 18.0 |
| Intervals of size four | 17.5 | 16.0 | 19.5 |

The modes have been computed by using the mid-point of the interval containing the largest frequency.

All three of these measures are central values and do not vary to any appreciable degree as the interval size is changed. The mid-ranges are lowest, the modes are highest, and the means are central to the other two. This centrality of the mean to the mode and mid-range tends to be true of many of the asymmetrical distributions found in practice, but does not hold for all possible distributions.

The mean can also be thought of in terms of relative frequencies. The relative frequency, symbolized by r, of a score value, x, is the ratio of the observed frequency to total frequency, i.e. $r_i = f_i/N$    (i = 1, 2, . . . k).

Since     $$\bar{X} = \frac{\Sigma f_i x_i}{N} = \frac{f_1 x_1}{N} \pm \frac{f_2 x_2}{N} \cdots + \frac{f_k x_k}{N}$$

then     $$\bar{X} = \Sigma r_i x_i = r_1 x_1 + r_2 x_2 + \ldots + r_k x_k$$

The mean can be calculated by multiplying each x value by its relative frequency and then adding. If percentage frequencies are more convenient, then the x values can be weighted by these numbers and the resulting sum divided by 100, since percentage frequencies are relative frequencies multiplied by 100.

The mean for the distribution of class sizes in Table 5 using percentage frequencies is:

$[(1.007)(8) + (4.096)(18) + \ldots + (3.728)(41) + (.638)(56)]$
$\div 100$ or $28/100 = 28.0$

The last central measure to be discussed is, in one sense, the most typical or most representative value in a distribution. This is the median which is defined: the value of the point on the scale of x such that fifty percent of the observed frequencies correspond with values of x below that point. Basically, the median is found by a counting process, which uses the order of the magnitudes of the score values occurring in the sample. In Table 1 there were 76 observations. Fifty percent is 38, so count up 38 frequencies. Up to and including $x = 17$, we find 36 frequencies. Since there are four eighteens, the median must be 18. Thinking of the underlying continuum of achievement, we realize that these four eighteens represent values from 17.5 to 18.5. If we assume that these four observations are evenly distributed over the interval, then the reasoning would proceed as follows:

a. Four scores are in the interval, 17.5–18.5.
b. The point having 38 scores below it is the point in this interval having 2 scores below it since 36 scores were below 17.5.
c. Assuming an even distribution this point must be 2/4 of the distance this interval covers.
d. This distance is one, so 2/4 of 1 is .5.
e. Consequently, the median is 17.5 + .5 equal to 18.

The assumption of an even distribution is not contradictory with the use of mid-points to represent the scores in an interval, since an even distribution of scores would result in their mass acting as if it were at the mid-point.

To calculate the median for the grouped distribution in Table 5, one again counts up 38 frequencies. This time it is found that 31 frequencies are below 13.5, while 48 are below 19.5. Hence, the median is in the interval, 16.5–19.5. Since 31 frequencies are below and 7 more are needed, the median is 7/17 of the distance into the interval. The total interval distance is 3; hence, 7/17 of 3 gives .4 of 3 or 1.2. The median is 16.5 + 1.2 or 17.7. This compares with the median of 18 calculated for the ungrouped distribution. Again, the grouping error is small.

The median class size in Table 4 could be computed by counting up the percentage frequencies to 50%. The reader can verify that the median is 29.9.

The four measures discussed are all central values and are all representative values in some sense. If we mean by "typical," the value of x most represented, the mode would be our typical value, but the mode does not wholly reflect the other values, which may account for a quite sizeable percent of the observed frequencies. An alternative way of defining "typical" is to seek the value of x which is "closest" to all the values. Close implies distance, so one is led to consideration of the distances, X, from T, where T is our typical value. One could pick a value for T and calculate the distances, $X_i - T$ ($i = 1, 2, \ldots k$). Some of these distances will be positive and some negative. When the distances for each of the score values are added, a cancelling effect results. To overcome this, the absolute values of the distances are added. The absolute value of a positive or negative number is its positive magnitude, and is symbolized by two lines, $|X_i - T|$. Of course, these distances should be weighted by the observed frequencies corresponding with each X value. Therefore, we calculate $\Sigma f_i |X_i - T|$. The typical value in a distribution can be defined as the value of T, which makes this sum a minimum. This minimizing value turns out to be the median!

To illustrate this, and, for convenience, just twenty observations, as shown in Table 6, are used.

TABLE 6

FREQUENCY DISTRIBUTION OF TWENTY VALUES

| X | f | $|x-5.75|$ | $f|x-5.75|$ | $|x-5.15|$ | $f|x-5.15|$ |
|---|---|---|---|---|---|
| 8 | 1 | 2.25 | 2.25 | 2.85 | 2.85 |
| 7 | 6 | 1.25 | 7.50 | 1.85 | 11.10 |
| 6 | 4 | .25 | 1.00 | .85 | 3.40 |
| 5 | 2 | .75 | 1.50 | .15 | .30 |
| 4 | 2 | 1.75 | 3.50 | 1.15 | 2.30 |
| 3 | 2 | 2.75 | 5.50 | 2.15 | 4.30 |
| 2 | 2 | 3.75 | 7.50 | 3.15 | 6.30 |
| 1 | 1 | 4.75 | 4.75 | 4.15 | 4.15 |
| | 20 | | 33.50 | | 34.70 |

The reader can verify that the median and mean of the distribution in Table 7 are 5.75 and 5.15, respectively. The absolute values of the distances of each score value from the median are shown in the third column, and these distances weighted by the frequencies are shown in the fourth column. The sum is 33.50. The corresponding calculations for the mean are shown in columns five and six. The sum of the weighted distances about the mean is 34.70. Similar calculations with the mode of 7 yields a sum of 38. This property of the median is true for any distribution. In some distributions, the sum of the weighted deviations around some other value might be as small as that for the median, but no other value can have a smaller sum. This justifies the statement that the median is the most typical or representative of the values in a distribution.

The purpose of the study determines which central value is reported after a set of data is collected. Of course, there is nothing wrong with reporting two or three central values, although some writers impress the fact of "putting all our eggs in one basket." This is nonsense. How one might be misled by reporting only one central value can be illustrated with a distribution such as family income. The mean family income in the United States during a certain year was roughly $7200, while the median family income for the same year was $5400. Two completely different impressions could be given the average consumer with these statistics. This divergence is due to the fact that family income is highly positively skewed. The mean is affected by the millionaires at the high end of the scale. Although relatively few in number, their inclusion in the calculation carries a great deal of weight.

A negatively skewed distribution has just the opposite relation between the mean and median. The mean is less than the median in this case. This also illustrates another reason why more than one central value should be reported. One receives a bonus in the form of a reasonable hypothesis about the form of the distribution.

Of the four central measures discussed, the mean and median are most often used. The median relies only on the order of the scores and has the property of typicality. The mean is affected by extreme scores, which is not only its weakness but its strength. Oftentimes, we want to focus on the aggregate—such as total achievement, or total tonnage shipped by a certain shipping company. If the mean tonnage per some time period were higher for one company than another, then that company would have shipped more material by weight, regardless of median tonnage. In addition, the mean has certain theoretical properties which favor its use. These will become more apparent later.

### Variability

One day a certain professor was extolling the virtues of essay examinations as compared with the multiple choice type. He was asked a question having to do with the reliability (or accuracy) with which he could score the papers. He replied that it was no trouble at all. He said, "I just read them, assign scores, give grades, and I've never been wrong yet." The moral to this story is: if you want to be right, use your own opinion only!

What would happen if another paper grader scored the same papers? Two opinions! What would happen if the papers were put away for awhile, given back to the professor to score again, without his being able to see the previous scoring marks? Again, two opinions! This has been demonstrated time and time again. If two observations are taken on any of an infinite number of variables, the two observations are likely to differ. Variability, or the non-constancy of effects, seems to be the rule. This variability can arise due to the nature of the variables or due to measurement error. Many readers may be shocked when learning that the so-called mathematical laws or constants in science have never been exactly fulfilled or measured. Even here (or especially here) one meets with variability. For "The Statistical View of Nature" the reader is referred to *Mathematics in Western Culture* by Morris Kline.[1] This view holds that the universal constants and "laws of nature" are merely average values of phenomena having probability distributions.

Two classes of students may be the same relative to mean intelligence, but, if the variability is larger in one class, the teacher is likely to have different problems than in the class where the variability is low. The graph below illustrates this situation. The means for distributions A

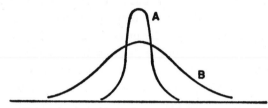

and B are nearly equivalent, but the variability or dispersion of scores is higher for B.

In fact, the modern view in education holds that the function of education is to make people more different or variable rather than more alike. This is the intended result of "homogeneous grouping."

There are several statistical measures of variability. Only two of them will be discussed. The first is the *range*, which is the difference between the highest and lowest observations. The ease of calculation of the range was demonstrated in the previous section, when the mid-range was considered. In addition to its calculational simplicity, it is functionally independent of central value. Suppose a distribution had a mean of thirty and another distribution had a mean of forty, nothing could be said of the range. The distribution with the higher mean may or may not have the higher range. (This is assuming no truncation of the scale.) Again, if one distribution had a range of nine and another a range of fourteen, nothing could be said concerning the central location of the two distributions. This is a necessary property of a statistical measure of variability, since merely reflecting central location all over again avails nothing.

The range does depend on the size of the sample, however. This seems strange, since sample size does not enter explicitly into its calculation! It happens in this way. Suppose there were one thousand students' test scores printed on cards and a sample of two cards was drawn at random. The difference (or range) of the test scores was then computed. Later, another sample was drawn from the original set of 1000 cards; this time

---

[1] Morris Kline, *Mathematics in Western Culture* (New York: Oxford University Press, 1953).

of size ten. The range of the ten scores was then computed. Since it is more likely to find one or two deviant observations in a sample of ten than it is in a sample of two, the second range is likely to be larger than the first. Not certain, but likely. If a sample of three hundred were drawn, it would be extremely likely that the range of these scores would be larger. Using certain assumptions about the form of the distribution of test scores, tables have been prepared which enable one to interpret ranges based on various sized samples, and so the range can still be useful.

Another statistic, which does not depend on central location but is directly interpreted as measuring variability about a central value, is the *standard deviation*. To measure dispersion about a central value, one is again led to consider distances, $x_i - a$, where "a" is the central value. The reasoning is: if the distribution has high variability, these distances, both positive and negative, should be large on the average. Rather than using absolute values to prevent the cancelling effect of positives and negatives after addition, the squares of the distances are used, i.e. $(X_i - a)^2$   $i = 1, 2, \ldots k$. The squares of both negative and positive numbers are positive. These squares are weighted by the frequencies, added, and then averaged, or $\dfrac{\Sigma f_i (X_i - a)^2}{N}$. The last step is to decide what central value should be used for "a." If the mean of the distribution is used, certain theoretical properties obtain. To name just two of them, this measure of variability is independent (in probability) of the mean and attains its minimum when the mean is used for "a."[2] Using the symbol, $S^2$, we have $S^2 = \dfrac{\Sigma f_i(X_i - \bar{X})^2}{N}$ $(i = 1, 2, \ldots k)$. If the variable X, is measured, say, in feet, then $S^2$ would be measured in square feet. Consequently, the square root of these squared deviations is taken, or

$$S = \sqrt{\dfrac{\Sigma f_i(X_i - \bar{X})^2}{N}}.$$ This measure, S, is called the *standard deviation* of the random variable, X, and $S^2$ is called the *variance*. (Sometimes it is more convenient to work with the variance rather than the standard deviation.)

Suppose the following five numbers were observed: 2, 3, 4, 5, 6. The mean of these numbers is 4. The deviations are $-2, -1, 0, +1, +2$ and the squared deviations are 4,1,0,1,4. Since each number occurs with frequency one, the squares are directly summed to give 10. Dividing by 5

---

[2] The first property is true only for normal distributions, while the second property is true for all distributions.

results in $S^2 = 2$. The standard deviation, S, is $\sqrt{2}$ or 1.414. The meaning of this number is, admittedly, vague to the reader who meets this statistic for the first time. Suffice it is to say that S is simply a measure of variability, nothing more or less. A richer meaning is to be found in the study of its properties.

Suppose another distribution of five numbers were observed: 1,2,4,6,7. How does the variability of these numbers compare with the five numbers above? Notice that the range is 6, while above the range was 4. At least, the two end numbers are further apart in the present case. Furthermore, the next two numbers towards the center, 2 and 6, are further apart than their counterparts, 3 and 5, in the first set of numbers. This is the kind of reasoning which enables one to answer the question regarding variability. The standard deviation is a statistic summarizing this reasoning. To calculate S, we notice the mean is again 4. The deviations are $-3$, $-2$, 0, $+2$, $+3$ and the squared deviations are 9, 4, 0, 4, 9. Summing and averaging gives 26/5 or 5.2. The variance, $S^2$, is 5.2 and the standard deviation, S, is $\sqrt{5.2}$ or 2.28. Comparing this figure with that found previously (1.414), it is seen that the variability is indeed larger.

If every observation in a frequency distribution were the same number, then S would be zero. Suppose thirty observations on an I.Q. test were taken, each one of them resulting in the number 105. The mean would be 105, and each of the deviations from the mean would be zero. Hence, S would be zero. This is the minimum value, since S can never be negative. Theoretically, there is no maximum value for S, but practically there is. If the range of the variable, X, is finite, then S is always less than or equal to one-half that range. For example, a test may yield scores from 0 to 50. That is, if a person answered every question wrong, his score would be 0 while answering every question right would give him a score of 50. Half the range would be 25, which is the maximum value for S calculated from observations yielded by this test. This maximum is attained, if half the scores are at one end of the scale and half are at the other end. If there are any in between, S will be even smaller.

The calculation of S can be tedious if the number of observations is large. By algebraic manipulation an alternative formula can be derived which shortens the work somewhat and which is convenient for desk calculaters. This formula is: $S^2 = \dfrac{\Sigma f_i X_i^2}{N} - \bar{X}^2$ or $S = \sqrt{\dfrac{\Sigma f_i X_i^2}{N} - \bar{X}^2}$

This formula requires two quantities met before, sample size, and mean, and one new quantity, the weighted sum of squares. The quantity, $\Sigma f_i X_i^2$, can be calculated by squaring each value of X, weighting by the frequency and then adding, or since $\Sigma f_i X_i^2 = \Sigma f_i X_i X_i$, it can be found by using the column containing $f_i X_i$ and simply multiplying again by $X_i$, $(i = 1, 2, \ldots k)$. This is shown in Table 5 of the preceding section for the distribution of test scores. The lowest value of X is 3. Squaring 3 gives 9 which is weighted by the frequency of 2 or $(2)(9) = 18$, which is the entry in the fifth column. The easier way is to use the entry in the fourth column, 6, and multiply again by $X = 3$ or $(6)(3) = 18$. The next entry is found in the same way or $(24)(6) = 144$. The column is then summed to 25236. Recall that the mean was 17.1 and $N = 76$.

Therefore, $\Sigma f_i X_i^2 = 25236$, $\bar{X} = 17.1$, $N = 76$

Then, $S^2 = \dfrac{25236}{76} - (17.1)^2$

$\quad\quad = 332.05 - 292.41$

$\quad\quad = 39.64$ and $S = \sqrt{39.64} = 6.31$

The variance is 39.64, and the standard deviation is 6.31.

Just as the mean of X was computed by weighting each X by the corresponding frequency, summing and dividing by N, the mean of $X^2$ would be computed by weighting each square by the frequency, summing and dividing by N. This is exactly what has been done above. The standard deviation can be thought of as the square root of the mean of the squares minus the square of the mean!

A useful approximation to the standard deviation is given by the formula $S \cong \dfrac{2(\Sigma X_U - \Sigma X_L)}{N}$ where $\Sigma X_U$ means the sum of the upper one-sixth of the observations and $\Sigma X_L$ means the sum of the lower one-sixth of the observations. The approximation is good for a large variety of distributions, but is best for distributions having a single mode near the mid-range of the observations. For the distribution of test scores which had $S = 6.31$, the approximation gives 6.61, which the reader may verify. Note that this distribution is somewhat bimodal, but the approximation is fairly good.

To illustrate the approximation, two distributions of word rate usage shown in Table 7 will be use. This data is taken from a study which investigated the disputed authorship of the *Federalist* papers.[3] The authors used forty-eight and fifty papers known to be written

---

[3] Frederick Mosteller, and David L. Wallace, "Inference in an Authorship Problem" *Journal of the American Statistical Association,* LVIII, June 1963, 275–309.

TABLE 7

FREQUENCY DISTRIBUTION OF RATE PER THOUSAND WORDS FOR 48
HAMILTON AND 50 MADISON PAPERS FOR THE WORD, *to*.
(Upper limit of a class interval is not included in the class.)

| Rate | f(Hamilton) | f(Madison) | Mid-points(x) |
|------|-------------|------------|---------------|
| 55–60 | 1 | | 57.5 |
| 50–55 | 2 | | 52.5 |
| 45–50 | 8 | 2 | 47.5 |
| 40–45 | 15 | 9 | 42.5 |
| 35–40 | 14 | 12 | 37.5 |
| 30–35 | 6 | 19 | 32.5 |
| 25–30 | 2 | 5 | 27.5 |
| 20–25 | | 3 | 22.5 |
| | 48 | 50 | |
| | $\bar{X} = 40.8$ | 35.0 | |
| | Md. = 40.7 | 34.5 | |

by Hamilton and Madison, respectively, in order to find differences in writing habits between these two men. Several word counts were taken. Table 7 shows the distribution of papers relative to the variable, rate per thousand words, for the single word, "to." The unit of measurement is to the last unit per thousand, so the bottom interval is 20–24.999 . . . or 20–25.

A quick inspection shows some apparent differences in the two men's writing habits, relative to this single word. The calculated means show that Hamilton, on the average, used "to" at the rate of 41 times per thousand words, while Madison's rate, on the average, was 35 times per thousand. Not a spectacular difference, but, when used in combination with other similar word differences, it can contribute to the discrimination of writing samples. The medians are also shown. Note that the use of the mode tends to magnify the difference.

To approximate S for Hamilton we find one-sixth of 48 which is 8. The sum of the upper and lower eight scores are found by using the mid-points. This is summarized below.

| *Upper* | | *Lower* | |
|---------|---|---------|---|
| 1(57.5) = | 57.5 | 2(27.5) = | 55.0 |
| 2(52.5) = | 105.0 | 6(32.5) = | 195.0 |
| 5(47.5) = | 237.5 | | |
| | 400.0 | | 250.0 |

Note that there were eight 47.5's, but we needed only five of them.

Substituting $S \cong \dfrac{2(400.00 - 250.0)}{48} \cong \dfrac{2(150.0)}{48} = \dfrac{150}{24} = 6.25.$ The

standard deviation is approximately 6.25. The actual standard deviation, calculated the long way, is 6.27.

For Madison's standard deviation, we proceed in the same way except that one-sixth of 50 is $8\frac{1}{3}$, or a mixed number. The only difference is that one-third of a mid-point is used after eight scores are accounted for.

| Upper | Lower |
|---|---|
| $2(47.5) = 95.0$ | $3(22.5) = 67.5$ |
| $6(42.5) = 255.0$ | $5(27.5) = 137.5$ |
| $\frac{1}{3}(42.5) = 14.2$ | $\frac{1}{3}(32.5) = 10.8$ |
| $364.2$ | $215.8$ |

Substituting: $S \cong \dfrac{2(364.2 - 215.8)}{50} \cong \dfrac{2(148.4)}{50} = \dfrac{148.4}{25} = 5.94.$ The

standard deviation is approximated to be 5.94. Calculation of S the long way yields the same result to two decimal places! It is interesting that even though these two writers differ in mean rates, median rates and modal rates for their use of the word, "to," they are almost the same with respect to the variability of use of this word. This might be interpreted to mean that these men write equally consistent with themselves.

### Percentiles and Percentile Ranks

The median of an observed distribution of observations on a random variable was previously defined as the value such that fifty percent of the observations were below that value. The median is a particular case of a class of statistics called percentiles of a distribution. In general, a percentile, symbolized by $P_x$, is the score such that x% of the scores are below $P_x$. For example $P_{75}$ is the seventy-fifth percentile and seventy-five percent of the scores are below $P_{75}$. The median is, thus, $P_{50}$.

Percentiles are calculated in the same way as a median, except that the particular percentage of frequencies counted varies from problem to problem. For the distribution in Table 1, $P_{75}$ is calculated as follows:

a. N = 76. 75% of 76 is 57.
b. Counting up 55 frequencies brings us to x = 21. Consequently, there are 55 frequencies below 21.5. Two more frequencies are needed.
c. There are 7 frequencies between 21.5 and 22.5.

d. Assuming an even distribution of these seven scores, we need $\frac{2}{7}$ of this interval or $\frac{2}{7}$ of $1 = 0.3$. Therefore, $P_{75}$ is $21.5 + 0.3 = 21.8$.

The calculation of $P_{25}$ is easier since 25% of 76 is 19, and nineteen scores can be counted without interpolation. The eighteenth and nineteenth scores are in the interval, $11.5 - 12.5$. Hence, $P_{25}$ is 12.5. Comparing $P_{25}$ and $P_{75}$ with the median, which was calculated previously, reveals the asymmetry of the distribution.

$$P_{75} = 21.8 \left.\right\} \text{ difference} = 3.8$$
$$P_{50} = 18.0$$
$$P_{25} = 12.5 \left.\right\} \text{ difference} = 5.5$$

Since the difference between $P_{50}$ and $P_{25}$ is roughly half again the difference between $P_{75}$ and $P_{50}$, the distribution is more variable in the lower half of the distribution than the upper half. This example illustrates the use of percentiles to describe frequency distributions.

A closely related statistic is the percentile rank. Symbolized by $PR_x$, the percentile rank of the score, x, is the percent of observations below the score x. When we find a percentile rank, we are finding a percent, but when we find a percentile, we are finding a score value. If $P_{50} = 18$, then the score value of 18 is such that 50% of the observations were below 18. Consequently, the percentile rank of 18 is 50 or $PR_{18} = 50$. A percentile rank is, in a sense, the opposite of a percentile.

To calculate the percentile rank of the score, 19, in Table 1 one needs to find the number of observations below 19.

a. Forty frequencies are below 18.5.
b. The score, 19, is half-way in the interval, $18.5 - 19.5$.
c. Assuming an even distribution of frequencies in the interval, we take half of the eight scores in the interval.
d. $\frac{1}{2}$ of $8 = 4$, so $4 + 40$ or 44 frequencies are below 19.
e. $\frac{44}{76} = .58$ or $PR_{19} = 58$.

One of the principal uses of percentile ranks is in the interpretation of test scores. Suppose a student's test score on a certain test is 67. This score by itself is not very informative. It may indicate poor, good, or average performance. If the mean and standard deviation of the class are known to be 55 and 10, respectively, one is able to say that the score indicates above average performance, since the score is 1.2 standard deviations above the mean. To a person experienced in the use of statistics this fact is informative, but to the student or his parent, it may not be. If the percentile rank of 67 is 82, it is known that this student scored higher than eighty-two percent of his classmates. This is a fact easily understood.

Another use of percentiles and percentile ranks is in the comparison of distributions. The respective means and standard deviations can be reported, but statistics relating various percentages of "overlap" to the two distributions can furnish a dramatic comparison. If it is reported that 20% of college seniors score below 50% of high school seniors on a general culture test, one can appreciate the overlap between the two test distributions. This statement says that the percentile rank in the college distribution of the high school median is 20. Similarly, if the percentile rank in the high school distribution of the college median is 90, then one knows that 90% of the high school seniors scored below 50% of the college seniors. Equivalently, 10% of the high school seniors scored above 50% of the college seniors. (This type of overlap has actually been observed between high school and college seniors.)

The calculations for grouped distributions are essentially the same as before. Using intervals of size three in Table 2, $P_{75}$ is found as follows:

a. 75% of 76 = 57.
b. Forty-eight frequencies are below 19.5. Nine more are needed.
c. Fourteen scores are in the interval, $19.5 - 22.5$, which is of length three.
d. $\frac{9}{14}$ of 3 = $\frac{27}{14}$ = 1.9. Hence $P_{75} = 19.5 + 1.9$ or 21.4.

This compares with 21.8 found in the ungrouped distribution which again demonstrates that the grouping error is small.

The percentile rank of the score, 19, is calculated as follows:

a. Thirty-one frequencies are below 16.5.
b. The score 19 is a distance of $19 - 16.5 = 2.5$ into the interval of size three.
c. Seventeen frequencies are in this interval.
d. $2.5/3$ of 17 = $42.5/3$ = 14.2.
e. There are $31 + 14.2$ or 44.2 scores below 19.
f. $44.2/76$ = .58 or $PR_{19}$ = 58.

### Standard Scores and the Chebychev Inequality

A convenient method of summarizing an individual's test score is to transform it to a *standard score*. The simplest standard score is one which expresses the test score in terms of standard deviation units. If a student achieved a score of 65 on a test which has a mean of 60 and a standard deviation of 5, then his score could be reported as $+1$ standard deviation, since his score is one standard deviation above the mean. Similarly, a score of 70 would be transformed to a standard score of $+2$. This type of standard score will be denoted by z and is defined as:

$$z = \frac{X - \bar{X}}{S}$$

Applying the formula for the score of 70 above gives:

$$z = \frac{70 - 60}{5} = \frac{10}{5} = 2$$

The z score corresponding to an x score of 50 would be:

$$z = \frac{50 - 60}{2} = \frac{-10}{5} = -2$$

A positive z score is interpreted as a number of standard deviations *above* the mean while a negative z score means the score is a certain number of standard deviations *below* the mean.

Suppose a student had taken three different tests with the following results:

|  | Test | | |
|---|---|---|---|
|  | 1 | 2 | 3 |
| Score (X) | 48 | 74 | 55 |
| $\bar{X}$ | 40 | 80 | 50 |
| S | 4 | 8 | 3 |

To interpret these scores, all nine numbers would be necessary if raw test scores, X, were used. Converting each score to a z score gives:

$$z_1 = \frac{48 - 40}{4} = \frac{8}{4} = 2$$

$$z_2 = \frac{74 - 80}{8} = \frac{-6}{8} = -.75$$

$$z_3 = \frac{55 - 50}{3} = \frac{5}{3} = 1.67$$

These three z scores of 2, $-.75$ and 1.67 are sufficient to summarize the test results. Using z scores, the means and standard deviations do not have to be reported for the purpose of interpretation of the test scores. Each of the z scores are on a standard scale with a mean of zero and a standard deviation of one, and, therefore, are comparable; whereas, the X scores are not directly comparable, since they are on scales with different means and standard deviations. Note that this student scored highest on test 2 relative to his raw X score, but that the z score indicates that he performed poorest on this test relative to the reference group from which the means and standard deviations were calculated.

The test results could also be summarized in terms of percentile ranks, but these measures have the disadvantage that proportional differences in raw scores on a test are not proportional to the differences in percentile ranks. Near the center of a bell-shaped distribution, a score distance of five points may correspond with a difference of twenty percentage points; while near the tails of the distribution this same distance of five points may correspond with a difference of seven percentage points. Differences in z scores are proportional to differences in x scores. A difference of five points anywhere on the x scale will result in the same difference in z scores. Percentile ranks are generally reported to students, parents, etc., while z scores are reported for statistical purposes.

Oftentimes, z scores are themselves transformed to more convenient scales. One such transformation is $Z = 10z + 50$. The "small" z score is transformed to a "big" Z score by multiplying by ten and adding fifty. If z scores are rounded to one decimal place, then Z scores are positive integers. The Z scores for the student's three scores given above are 70, 42, and 67. The mean and standard deviation of a Z scale are 50 and 10, respectively. The use of Z rather than z introduces no new information. They are merely a convenience. College board scores are reported by using $C = 100z + 500$. These "C scores" have a mean of 500 and a standard deviation of 100. A student, earning a college board score of 550, scored a half standard deviation above the mean, or his z score was .5. To change C scores or Z scores back to z scores, do just the opposite of what the reporting agency did. For a C score 500 was added, so subtract 500 giving 50. They multiplied by 100, so you divide by 100 giving $50/100 = .5$.

One use of standard scores is in forming composite scores. If two tests have been administered during a grading period, teachers usually desire to form some kind of score which includes or reflects each single test performance, but which will also reflect the "total" performance. It would seem that the simple sum of the two test scores would be sufficient, but this is not an optimal procedure. Consider two students whose test scores on two tests are shown below together with the means and standard deviations.

| Student | Test A | $z_A$ | Test B | $z_B$ | Composite A + B | $z_A + z_B$ |
|---------|--------|-------|--------|-------|------------------|-------------|
| 1 | 30 | 0 | 50 | +2 | 80 | 2 |
| 2 | 40 | +1 | 40 | 0 | 80 | 1 |
| $\bar{X}$ | 30 | | 40 | | | |
| S | 10 | | 5 | | | |

If the two test scores are added, it would appear that the test performances of these students are equivalent, since the composite score for each student is 80. The z scores show otherwise, however. Student 1 scored at the mean on the first test, but showed outstanding performance on the second test. Student 2 scored at the mean on the second test, and, while above the mean on the first test, his score was not outstanding. Consequently, adding the z scores to form a composite score suggests that student 1 had higher over-all performance than student 2. Since the two procedures—adding raw test scores and adding z scores—lead to different conclusions, the teacher who desires a composite score should be aware of the assumptions and consequences of each procedure.

The basic issue involved is the definition of "comparability." If raw scores are added, one is assuming that one point on the first test is comparable with or equivalent to one point on the second test. An analogy is the measurement of two different lengths with two different rulers, each ruler calibrated in inches. One inch at one measurement is comparable with one inch at another measurement. With test scores, we are dealing with units of "achievement" which are *arbitrarily* assigned, when it is decided how many points each item should be worth. That is, if item #1 is scored zero if the student answers incorrectly and one if the student answers correctly, then we are implicitly scaling the amount of "achievement" represented by item #2 as equal to the amount required to answer item #1. If two points were assigned to item #2, then the scaling would be in the ratio 2 to 1. When we add the item scores to obtain a test score, we are actually forming a score which is a composite of the item scores. Therefore, there are actually two related questions: (1) how should the test items be combined to form a test score? and (2) how should the scores from different tests be combined into an over-all composite score?

Fortunately, the first question has an easy answer. If the number of items is large (twenty or more), and, if the weights assigned to each item are not too different (less than 3 to 1 for any two items), then the resulting test scores will rank and scale the students about the same as other test scores resulting from the use of different weightings. This fact justifies the use of equal weightings—that is, merely assigning each item one point.

Two further implications can be drawn. First, if we desire to form an over-all composite score from the scores on twenty or more tests, then thinking of the individual tests like individual items on one test, we could apply the above fact and conclude that it doesn't make too much difference how we weight the tests (as long as they are weighted three to one or less.) The easiest weighting to choose is that of using equal weights, so with a large number of tests, one could merely add the test scores. Of course, if just two tests have been administered then we cannot routinely use this same reasoning.

The second implication, however, is that if we do merely add the two test scores, then we are acting as if we actually had one long test instead of two shorter ones. If the first test had twenty items and the second test had thirty items, then we could think of these tests as being one long test of fifty items. Since differential item weightings are relatively unimportant, one could simply weight each item equally and just total the number correct. This procedure would be equivalent to adding the two test scores to form an over-all composite score.

It would appear that both questions posed above have been answered. The difficulty, however, is that we do not always want to assume that two different tests are actually one longer test. Each test has its own errors of measurement, since the individuals and conditions of testing are not psychologically or physically the same from one test to another. Oftentimes, we want to preserve the individual identity of the two tests. It is in these cases that z scores are used to form composite scores. The use of z scores avoids defining one point on test #1 as comparable with one point on test #2. Rather, the definition of comparability is in terms of the variability of the group's scores about the mean of the group. Referring back to the example of the two students, Test A is twice as variable as Test B in terms of standard deviation units. This means that the students are more heterogeneous on Test A and/or the points were inflated on Test A. If two points had been assigned to each item on Test B rather than one, the standard deviation on Test B would also have been 10. To avoid this kind of inflation and to equalize heterogeneity on both tests, z scores may be used. The net result is that a score of 40 on Test A is then comparable to a score of 45 on Test B, since these two scores each have z scores of $+1$. Similarly, a score of 28 on Test A is comparable with a score of 39 on Test B, since the two z scores each are $-0.2$.

To summarize:

1. Item weightings on any one test are relatively unimportant.
2. If many test scores are to be combined, one can simply add the scores to form a composite.
3. If a few tests are to be combined, then:
   a. Add the raw scores, if individual identity of tests is not important.
   b. Add z scores to maintain identity and remove the effects of arbitrary inflations of scoring.

One should note that when test scores are forced to be on a percentage scale of 100, that the scores are usually inflated, and, hence, the variability is changed. If the test consists of twenty items, and, if a percentage scale is used, each item is given five points rather than one. Using z scores in this case would adjust for the arbitrary inflation of scores. The author recommends the use of z scores in almost all cases.

This method of forming composite scores can be extended to any number of tests and any combination of weights. If three tests have been administered and it is desired to weight the third test by 2, then form scores, $z_A + z_B + 2z_C$. The reader is cautioned that composites formed in this way are not z scores themselves, but this fact does not detract from their usefulness.

In the past few sections a number of statistical tools has been presented, the emphasis being on the description of data arranged in frequency distributions. The concept of sampling was implied, but no direct references to the theory of probability were made. Now, however, a connection between statistical theory and probability can be made.

The basis is a random variable with some distribution of probabilities. This distribution has a well-defined mean and standard deviation. The Greek letter, $\mu$, pronounced "mew" will symbolize the mean, while, $\sigma$, pronounced "sigma" will symbolize the standard deviation. (Note that $\Sigma$ is the capital form of $\sigma$.) Greek letters are used to emphasize that they refer to a theoretical mean and standard deviation of a population. The word, population, is used because the probability distribution referred to is often thought of as corresponding to the relative frequencies of values of a variable in a large group or "population" of people. For example, one might think of the I.Q.'s of all the children in a certain political sub-division as defining a population or probability distribution of the variable,

I.Q. The relative frequencies with which each value of I.Q. occurs is accepted as the true probability. From this population, a sample of children might be tested and observed frequencies obtained. This sampling is thought of as equivalent to the tossing of a die several times (as discussed in Chapter II). Observing a number on the die is equivalent to observing a value of the variable, I.Q.

A Russian in 1890 proved a remarkable fact about all probability distributions. His name was Chebyshev, and today we call his theorem, Chebyshev's inequality. If x is a random variable with mean, $\mu$, and standard deviation, $\sigma$, then the total probability of all values of x within standard deviations about the mean is at least $1 - 1/k^2$. Symbolically:

$$\text{Prob } ( -k\,\sigma \leqq x - \mu \leqq k\,\sigma) > 1 - 1/k^2$$

To use the inequality, a value of k is selected. Suppose k is equal to two. The inequality will give a lower bound to the probability of observing a value of the random variable within two standard deviations of the mean. Substituting k = 2:

$$\text{Prob } (-2\sigma \leqq x - \mu \leqq 2\sigma) > 1 - \tfrac{1}{4} = \tfrac{3}{4}$$

The inequality shows that this probability must be at least $\tfrac{3}{4}$ or .75. The remarkable fact is that this is true for all probability distributions (having a mean and standard deviation).

If all that was known about a distribution of a random variable was that it had a mean of 100 and a standard deviation of 10, the inequality would tell the reviewer that at least 75% of the probability was concentrated between 80 and 120. To find the lower bound of the amount of probability between 70 and 130 k = 3 is used. Substituting gives $1 - \tfrac{1}{9}$ or $\tfrac{8}{9}$ equal to .89. For sample distributions the inequality can be written as:

$$\text{Prob } ( -k \leqq z \leqq k) > 1 - 1/k^2$$

In this form, it can be calculated, for example, that at least 75% of sample values have z scores between $-2$ and $+2$. Knowing only a z score, then, allows one to put lower bounds on the percentile rank of that z score. A z score of $+2$ must have percentile rank of 75% or greater. If the distribution were symmetrical, then the 25% outside $-2$ and $+2$ could be split into equal parts of 12.5%. This would allow one to say that the minimum percentile rank of z = $+2$ is 87.5%, since there could be no more than 12.5% above z = $+2$. Table 8 shows probabilities or percentages of frequencies in a sample for various other values of k.

TABLE 8

PROBABILITIES OR PERCENTAGES FROM CHEBYSHEV'S INEQUALITY

| k | Probabilities or percentages within k. Standard deviations of the mean. |
|---|---|
| 1.0 | 0 |
| 1.1 | .17 |
| 1.3 | .47 |
| 1.5 | .56 |
| 1.7 | .65 |
| 2.0 | .75 |
| 2.2 | .79 |
| 2.5 | .84 |
| 3 | .89 |
| 4 | .93 |
| 5 | .96 |

The importance of Chebyshev's inequality is mainly theoretical, but it illustrates the intimate connection between statistics such as z scores and the theory of probability. Remember that these probabilities are only lower bounds. If one knows the actual probability distribution, much stronger statements can be made. The inequality is true, however, for even the most irregular distributions one could imagine.

## The Normal Distribution

Many people have had height measured at one time or another—usually in a doctor's office. A measuring device commonly used is a platform scale—one to measure weight with an attached vertical scale to measure height. A movable vertical rod with a horizontal extension is adjusted so that the horizontal bar is touching the top-most portion of one's head. The nurse reads the height by comparing a mark on the movable rod with the fixed vertical scale, which is graduated to fractions of an inch (or other unit of measure).

Is the height that is recorded by the nurse true height at that time? The answer depends on what is meant by "true" height. But one thing is sure. If one's height is re-measured immediately after a first measuring, a different height is likely to be found. This is assuming that the nurse re-measures in an "objective" manner. Oftentimes, people will tend to perceive what they want to perceive, and the same measurement will be reported again even though the scale says otherwise! Another nurse could be asked to measure the same person's height, without being informed what height the first nurse found—thereby eliminating the psychological effect biasing repeated measurement by the same person. Unfortunately, here, however, a new effect is introduced. This effect could be thought of as that which may differ one nurse from another in measuring technique—adjusting the bar, reading the scale, etc. Other effects would operate, such as how straight the subject stands, how much pressure is exerted by the nurse in adjusting the horizontal bar, how "bushy" the subject's hair is, etc. If the nurse exerts too much pressure on the top of one's head, causing an almost imperceptible relaxing, it could result in a "short" measurement.

One may or may not be concerned with these errors of measurement. If one's height was known to be between four feet and seven feet before stepping on the scale, it is implied that a more accurate measurement is required. If height is measured within two inches, this may be sufficient. The concern one has is related to what purposes were in mind for the measurement result.

Now suppose that whatever the magnitude of error involved, that the error operates in a random fashion. That is, we do not consistently stand "short" or "tall," but sometimes relax, sometimes stiffen in a pattern which would resemble the successive tosses of a coin—a heads denoting short, a tails denoting tall. The nurse or nurses also operate randomly— not consistently pressing the bar tightly but leaving it loose at times. If we were measured one-hundred times, what might the distribution of these measurements resemble? First, since the errors are random, it could reasonably be expected that about half of the measurements would be at or above our true height and half at or below. Second, it could be expected that small errors would occur more frequently than large ones. If there are several causes of disturbance operating, some of them may, in effect, cancel each other. Only, if the several causes all worked in one direction would a relatively large error be observed, and this is not as likely as when some factors are operating one way, others are operating the other way.

The distribution of the measurement, then, is symmetrical about our true height, with ever-decreasing frequency further and further away from our true height. This type of reasoning leads one to the normal distribution, shown below; this serves as a model for many distributions of repeated measurements.

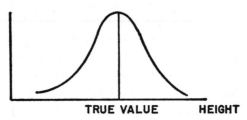

TRUE VALUE       HEIGHT

The normal distribution, or normal curve, has been known since the early nineteenth century, at least. It is sometimes referred to as the Gaussian error curve after the mathematician, Gauss (1777–1855), who systematically studied the theory of errors. It was thought at that time that all random error was distributed normally, but this is not a true generalization. Depending on the assumptions made, other distributions are possible.

The fact that many distributions of various variables were found distributed according to the normal distribution led researchers of the nineteenth century, such as Quetelet, a Belgian scientist, to the conclusion that all variables were distributed normally. If they were not observed to be quite normal, then something was wrong with the measurement system, or some extraneous factor was postulated. If a mental test did not yield scores which were normal, then the fault must be in the test, since the normal curve was a "natural" or "normal" distribution. Today, it is known that there are several distributions possible and, in fact, they can be observed. The question of what is "natural" has no answer, since the very act of man observing nature forever confounds the "natural" effect. Kronecker, an early mathematician, said, "God made the integers, the rest is the work of man." Today, we would say Kronecker undergeneralized.

The normal distribution remains a useful tool for statisticians. First, many variables do seem to be normally distributed. Variables such as height, head girth, and repeated measurements on other physical constants serve as examples. Furthermore, even if the distribution of a variable is not exactly normal, the assumption of a normal distribution is oftentimes convenient and does not result in appreciable error.

The formula for the normal curve contains two parameters. These parameters are the mean, $\mu$, and the standard deviation, $\sigma$, or equivalently, the variance, $\sigma^2$. The substitution of particular values for $\mu$ and $\sigma^2$ in the normal curve formula results in a normal curve which is one of a family of all possible normal curves. Figure 6 shows two normal curves. Curves (a) and (b) are both normal curves with means of 100, but (a) has a standard deviation of 5 while (b) has a standard deviation of 10. If a different value for the mean is substituted, then the curve is shifted up or down the scale.

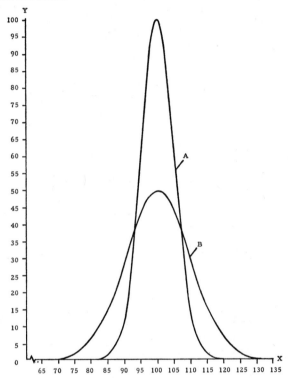

Figure 6. Two Normal Distributions with $\mu = 100$, $\sigma = 5$, (A) and $\sigma = 10$, (B)

Several properties of the normal curve should be noted. First, the distribution is symmetrical with its mean, median, and mode equal. Second, almost all of the area under a normal curve is between $3\sigma$ below the mean and $3\sigma$ above the mean. For curve (a) these points are 85 and 115 and for curve (b), 70 and 130. The range of a normal curve is actually from minus infinity to plus infinity, but the area outside z of $-3$ and $+3$ accounts for only twenty-seven hundredths of one percent of the total area. Third, the area under one normal curve between any two z scores relative to that curve is the same as that under a second normal curve between the same two z scores relative to the second curve. Between the mean ($z = 0$) and one standard deviation above the mean ($z = 1$), thirty-four percent of the total area is found. Since fifty percent is below the mean, eighty-four percent of the total area is below $z = 1$. If two test score distributions were normal (at least approximately) such as curves (a) and (b), then the percentile rank of the score, 105, would be 84 in distribution (a) but the score in distribution (b) with percentile rank, 84, would be 110.

Table 9 gives the fraction of the total area under a normal curve with mean of zero and standard deviation of one. To use this table for a normally distributed variable, x, one must first make the z transformation.

TABLE 9

AREA OF THE STANDARD NORMAL DISTRIBUTION

| z | .00 | .02 | .04 | .06 | .08 |
|---|---|---|---|---|---|
| .0 | .500 | .508 | .516 | .524 | .532 |
| .1 | .540 | .548 | .556 | .564 | .571 |
| .2 | .579 | .587 | .595 | .603 | .610 |
| .3 | .618 | .626 | .633 | .641 | .648 |
| .4 | .655 | .663 | .670 | .677 | .684 |
| .5 | .691 | .698 | .705 | .712 | .719 |
| .6 | .726 | .732 | .739 | .745 | .752 |
| .7 | .758 | .764 | .770 | .776 | .782 |
| .8 | .788 | .794 | .800 | .805 | .811 |
| .9 | .816 | .821 | .826 | .831 | .836 |
| 1.0 | .841 | .846 | .851 | .855 | .860 |
| 1.1 | .864 | .869 | .873 | .877 | .881 |
| 1.2 | .885 | .889 | .893 | .896 | .900 |
| 1.3 | .903 | .907 | .910 | .913 | .916 |
| 1.4 | .919 | .922 | .925 | .928 | .931 |
| 1.5 | .933 | .936 | .938 | .941 | .946 |
| 1.6 | .945 | .947 | .949 | .952 | .954 |
| 1.7 | .955 | .957 | .959 | .961 | .962 |
| 1.8 | .964 | .966 | .967 | .969 | .970 |
| 1.9 | .971 | .973 | .974 | .975 | .976 |
| 2.0 | .977 | .978 | .979 | .980 | .981 |
| 2.1 | .982 | .983 | .984 | .985 | .985 |
| 2.2 | .986 | .987 | .987 | .988 | .989 |
| 2.3 | .989 | .990 | .990 | .991 | .991 |
| 2.4 | .992 | .992 | .993 | .993 | .993 |
| 2.5 | .994 | .994 | .994 | .995 | .995 |

Reprinted from D. B. Owen, *Handbook of Statistical Tables* (Reading, Mass.: Addison-Wesley, Inc., 1962), p. 3. By permission of the author and publishers.

Since the normal curve is symmetrical, only positive z values are shown. Examples of using the table are shown below. The first decimal figure of z is read in the first vertical column and the second decimal figure is read in the first horizontal row. (Throughout, it is assumed the variable is normally distributed.)

1. Find the percentile rank of z = 1.4. Enter the table with z = 1.4 in the first column and .00 in the first row (i.e. z = 1.40) and read .919. Therefore, the percentile rank is 91.9 or 92.
2. Find the percentile rank of z = −.82.
   (a) Enter the table with z = .8 in the first column and .02 in the first row and read .794. This is the fraction of area from minus infinity up to z = .82.
   (b) The fraction of area in the shaded portion of the upper tail is 1 − .794 = .206.
   (c) Since the curve is symmetrical, the fraction of area below z = −.82 equals that above z = .82. Therefore, the percentile rank of z = −.82 is 21.6 or 22.
3. Find the percent of area *between* z = −.82 and z = .82.
   (a) The fraction of area in each tail is .206 (found above). Therefore, the area in both tails is .206 + .206 = .412.
   (b) The area between these points is 1 − .412 = .588 or 58.8% of the area is between −.82 and +.82.
4. Find the fraction of area between −.36 and +.82.

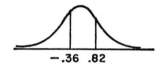

   **−.36  .82**

   (a) The fraction of area below +.82 is .794, therefore, the fraction of area between 0 and +.82 is .794 − .500 = .294.
   (b) The fraction of area below +.36 is .641. Therefore, .141 is between 0 and +.36.
   (c) By symmetry, .141 is between 0 and −.36.
   (d) The fraction of area between −.36 and +.82 is .294 + .141 = .435.
5. If a test has a mean of 50 and standard deviation of 4, what is the percentile rank of a score of 56?
   (a) Transform to $z = \dfrac{56-50}{4} = \%4 = 1.50$.
   (b) Enter table with 1.50 and read answer of .933 or $PR_{56}$ = 93.

Since many tests do yield scores which are normally distributed, one can use Table 9 to help interpret standard scores.

As pointed out earlier, people were guilty of over-generalizing the normal distribution. One of these over-generalizations, important to education, concerns the distribution of intelligence. Stanford-Binet I.Q. scores are normally distributed with a mean of approximately 100 and standard deviation of about 16. Should the conclusion be made that intelligence is normally distributed? If intelligence is "that which the test measures," then the answer is "Yes"! However, if reference is to a concept or trait existing independently of the test, the answer is "Maybe, maybe not." It would seem that people who talk about the distribution of intelligence being a "universal" distribution *are* referring to intelligence independently of any test, and, therefore, are in error when they claim a particular form of distribution. The point of the whole matter is that the test constructor forces the test to give a normal distribution! He does this by selecting items, trying them out, gathering statistics relative to item difficulty and discrimination power, and retaining or dropping the items meeting or not meeting his specifications. The distribution of the trait "intelligence" could be positively skewed, yet the test scores would be normally distributed. It is understandable that in the history of science people have over-generalized and have read grand order and design into facts—such as the path of all planets around the sun being ellipses (approximately). It is less understandable to realize this happening in the field of mental testing, where man so obviously intrudes.

# CHAPTER IV

# Sampling Distributions

## Sample Estimators of a Population Mean

Sometimes the data collected in connection with a certain study is considered as the whole of the statistical population. The distribution of class sizes in elementary schools presented in Chapter II is such an example. Virtually all of the elementary classes were included, and our interest was confined to a description of the resulting frequency distribution. The distribution of test scores for a particular class may be considered also as forming a population.

Oftentimes, the collected data is thought of as a sample from some larger population. A distribution of class sizes could have been obtained from a random sample of fifty percent of the total number of classes. Then our interest would extend beyond description of the sample to questions involving description of the population of classes. Again, a sample of children might be tested to yield information regarding some larger group or population of children. Sometimes a probability model is formulated for some mechanism or phenomenon, and data relevant to the problem is analyzed as a sample of observations from a population probability distribution. A simple example is the tossing of a six-sided die which would generate a sample distribution such as discussed in Chapter II.

When a sample distribution is under study, the sample statistics are examined relative to their descriptive properties as well as to their inferential properties, i.e., the amount and kinds of information they can furnish regarding the population.

By using a small population of nine numbers as shown in Table 10 some of these properties will be analyzed. The mean and variance are calculated for the population as $\mu = 3$ and $\sigma^2 = 1.5$. The symbol, $\mu$ and $\sigma^2$, are used to emphasize that these numbers are considered as parameters of the statistical population. Notice also that the population variance is defined slightly different from the definition of variance used earlier. Previously, the variance was defined as the sum of the weighted squared

TABLE 10

FINITE POPULATION OF NUMBERS

| x | f | fx | fx$^2$ |
|---|---|----|--------|
| 5 | 1 | 5 | 25 |
| 4 | 2 | 8 | 32 |
| 3 | 3 | 9 | 27 |
| 2 | 2 | 4 | 8 |
| 1 | 1 | 1 | 1 |
|   | 9 | 27 | 93 |

$$\mu = \frac{\Sigma fx}{N} = \frac{27}{9} = 3$$

$$\sigma^2 = \frac{\Sigma f(x-\mu)^2}{N-1} = \frac{\Sigma fx^2}{N-1} - \frac{(\Sigma fx)^2}{N(N-1)}$$

$$= \frac{93}{8} - \frac{(27)^2}{9(8)} = 11.625 - 10.125$$

$$\sigma^2 = 1.5$$

deviations divided by N. In the present case we divide by N–1. This is merely a matter of convenience, since it will result in somewhat simpler algebraic formulae. (The similarly revised computational formula is also shown.)

Suppose a random sample of three of the nine population numbers is taken. What information about the population can be gained by examining these three numbers? To gain some insight into this question, let us consider all possible samples of size n = 3 from the population of N = 9 numbers. (Capital N will refer to the population, while lower-case n will refer to the sample). Rather than use the population numbers for tabulation of all possible samples, letters representing the numbers will be used to minimize confusion. The coding is:

| a | b | c | d | e | f | g | h | i |
|---|---|---|---|---|---|---|---|---|
| 1 | 2 | 2 | 3 | 3 | 3 | 4 | 4 | 5 |

For example, bcg, represents the drawing of both twos and the first four −2,2,4. For each sample the mean ($\bar{x}$), median (Md) and mid-range (MR) are calculated. The eighty-four possible samples are shown in Table 11.

The samples were generated systematically by first writing all samples which include "a." Within these samples, all samples containing "ab" were listed, then "ac," then "ad," etc. Changing the first letter to "b," samples containing "bc," "bd," etc. were generated. This continues until

## TABLE 11
### Samples of Three from Population of Table 10

| Sample | Numbers | $\bar{X}$ | Md | MR |
|--------|---------|-----------|------|------|
| abc | 122 | 1.667 | 1.75 | 1.5 |
| abd | 123 | 2.000 | 2.00 | 2.0 |
| abe | 123 | 2.000 | 2.00 | 2.0 |
| abf | 123 | 2.000 | 2.00 | 2.0 |
| abg | 124 | 2.333 | 2.00 | 2.5 |
| abh | 124 | 2.333 | 2.00 | 2.5 |
| abi | 125 | 2.667 | 2.00 | 3.0 |
| acd | 123 | 2.000 | 2.00 | 2.0 |
| ace | 123 | 2.000 | 2.00 | 2.0 |
| acf | 123 | 2.000 | 2.00 | 2.0 |
| acg | 124 | 2.333 | 2.00 | 2.5 |
| ach | 124 | 2.333 | 2.00 | 2.5 |
| aci | 125 | 2.667 | 2.00 | 3.0 |
| ade | 133 | 2.333 | 2.75 | 2.0 |
| adf | 133 | 2.333 | 2.75 | 2.0 |
| adg | 134 | 2.667 | 3.00 | 2.5 |
| adh | 134 | 2.667 | 3.00 | 2.5 |
| adi | 135 | 3.000 | 3.00 | 3.0 |
| aef | 133 | 2.333 | 2.75 | 2.0 |
| aeg | 134 | 2.667 | 3.00 | 2.5 |
| aeh | 134 | 2.667 | 3.00 | 2.5 |
| aei | 135 | 3.000 | 3.00 | 3.0 |
| afg | 134 | 2.667 | 3.00 | 2.5 |
| afh | 134 | 2.667 | 3.00 | 2.5 |
| afi | 135 | 3.000 | 3.00 | 3.0 |
| agh | 144 | 3.000 | 3.75 | 2.5 |
| agi | 145 | 3.333 | 4.00 | 3.0 |
| ahi | 145 | 3.333 | 4.00 | 3.0 |
| bcd | 223 | 2.333 | 2.25 | 2.5 |
| bce | 223 | 2.333 | 2.25 | 2.5 |
| bcf | 223 | 2.333 | 2.25 | 2.5 |
| bcg | 224 | 2.667 | 2.25 | 3.0 |
| bch | 224 | 2.667 | 2.25 | 3.0 |
| bci | 225 | 3.000 | 2.25 | 3.5 |
| bde | 233 | 2.667 | 2.75 | 2.5 |
| bdf | 233 | 2.667 | 2.75 | 2.5 |
| bdg | 234 | 3.000 | 3.00 | 3.0 |
| bdh | 234 | 3.000 | 3.00 | 3.0 |
| bdi | 235 | 3.333 | 3.00 | 3.5 |
| bef | 233 | 2.667 | 2.75 | 2.5 |
| beg | 234 | 3.000 | 3.00 | 3.0 |
| beh | 234 | 3.000 | 3.00 | 3.0 |
| bei | 235 | 3.333 | 3.00 | 3.5 |
| bfg | 234 | 3.000 | 3.00 | 3.0 |
| bfh | 234 | 3.000 | 3.00 | 3.0 |
| bfi | 235 | 3.333 | 3.00 | 3.5 |
| bgh | 244 | 3.333 | 3.75 | 3.0 |
| bgi | 245 | 3.667 | 4.00 | 3.5 |

| Sample | Numbers | $\bar{X}$ | Md | MR |
|--------|---------|-----------|------|------|
| bhi | 245 | 3.667 | 4.00 | 3.5 |
| cde | 233 | 2.667 | 2.75 | 2.5 |
| cdf | 233 | 2.667 | 2.75 | 2.5 |
| cdg | 234 | 3.000 | 3.00 | 3.0 |
| cdh | 234 | 3.000 | 3.00 | 3.0 |
| cdi | 235 | 3.333 | 3.00 | 3.5 |
| cef | 233 | 2.667 | 2.75 | 2.5 |
| ceg | 234 | 3.000 | 3.00 | 3.0 |
| ceh | 234 | 3.000 | 3.00 | 3.0 |
| cei | 235 | 3.333 | 3.00 | 3.5 |
| cfg | 234 | 3.000 | 3.00 | 3.0 |
| cfh | 234 | 3.000 | 3.00 | 3.0 |
| cfi | 235 | 3.333 | 3.00 | 3.5 |
| cgh | 244 | 3.333 | 3.75 | 3.0 |
| cgi | 245 | 3.667 | 4.00 | 3.5 |
| chi | 245 | 3.667 | 4.00 | 3.5 |
| def | 333 | 3.000 | 3.00 | 3.0 |
| deg | 334 | 3.333 | 3.25 | 3.5 |
| deh | 334 | 3.333 | 3.25 | 3.5 |
| dei | 335 | 3.667 | 3.25 | 4.0 |
| dfg | 334 | 3.333 | 3.25 | 3.5 |
| dfh | 334 | 3.333 | 3.25 | 3.5 |
| dfi | 335 | 3.667 | 3.25 | 4.0 |
| dgh | 344 | 3.667 | 3.75 | 3.5 |
| dgi | 345 | 4.000 | 4.00 | 4.0 |
| dhi | 345 | 4.000 | 4.00 | 4.0 |
| efg | 334 | 3.333 | 3.25 | 3.5 |
| efh | 334 | 3.333 | 3.25 | 3.5 |
| efi | 335 | 3.667 | 3.25 | 4.0 |
| egh | 344 | 3.667 | 3.75 | 3.5 |
| egi | 345 | 4.000 | 4.00 | 4.0 |
| ehi | 345 | 4.000 | 4.00 | 4.0 |
| fgh | 344 | 3.667 | 3.75 | 3.5 |
| fgi | 345 | 4.000 | 4.00 | 4.0 |
| fhi | 345 | 4.000 | 4.00 | 4.0 |
| ghi | 445 | 4.333 | 4.25 | 4.5 |

"g" is used for the first letter yielding the one sample, ghi. The first letters are always paired with letters that follow in the alphabet. This insures that all samples will be included *with no duplications*. The sample, "bca," is not different from "abc," for example. Similarly, no samples would be written with "hi" in the first two positions, since any further permutation of the letters would duplicate a sample already written. The horizontal lines have been drawn in Table 11 after each change of letter in the first or second column to aid the reader in seeing the system used.

To summarize, all possible samples of n = 3 numbers from a population of N = 9 numbers have been written. Even though a systematic ordering has been used to generate these samples, the particular order of the three numbers in a sample is irrelevant. Each sample consists of a different combination of three numbers. One could think of the nine numbers as being the scores of students. Each sample consists of a particular combination of three students, and no two samples consist of the same three students.

The numbers corresponding to the letters are shown in column two and the means for each sample are given in the third column. These means are arranged in a frequency distribution in Table 12.

TABLE 12

FREQUENCY DISTRIBUTION OF MEANS
FOR
SAMPLES OF SIZE THREE

| $\bar{X}$ | f | f$\bar{X}$ | f$\bar{X}^2$ |
|---|---|---|---|
| 4.333 | 1 | 4.333 | 18.775 |
| 4.000 | 6 | 24.000 | 96.000 |
| 3.667 | 10 | 36.670 | 134.469 |
| 3.333 | 16 | 53.328 | 177.742 |
| 3.000 | 18 | 54.000 | 162.000 |
| 2.667 | 16 | 42.672 | 113.806 |
| 2.333 | 10 | 23.330 | 54.429 |
| 2.000 | 6 | 12.000 | 24.000 |
| 1.667 | 1 | 1.667 | 2.779 |
|  | 84 | 252.000 | 784.000 |

Notice that the means form a symmetrical distribution about the value, 3.000. Since the population was symmetrical about this same value, this feature of the distribution of means is not surprising. It can be seen, then, that the mean of the means, $\bar{\bar{X}}$, is 3.000. This is verified by calculation of $\Sigma f\bar{X}/84 = 252.000/84 = 3$. Furthermore, notice that the means are less variable than the population numbers. The population ranged from 1 to 5 while the means range from 1.667 to 4.333. It should be expected, then, that the variance and standard deviation of the means is less than that calculated for the population. This direct comparison would require the variance of the means to be calculated using 83 rather than 84 as the divisor for the weighted sums of squares, since the population variance was defined in terms of N–1. This calculation will not be shown, however.

Instead, calculating the variance of the sample means will be done in

the usual way, i.e., $S_{\bar{X}}^2 = \dfrac{\Sigma f_i(\bar{x}_i - \bar{\bar{X}})^2}{84} = \dfrac{\Sigma f \bar{X}^2}{84} - \bar{\bar{x}}^2$

The subscript, $\bar{X}$, on $S_{\bar{X}}^2$ is used to show that this variance is a variance of means. Also, notice that the squared deviations are calculated from the deviations of each mean around the mean of the means. The usual computation formula is also shown. This calculation yields:

$$S_{\bar{X}}^2 = \frac{784.000}{84} - (3)^2$$

$$= 9.333 - 9$$

$$= .333$$

The variance of the sample means, $S_{\bar{X}}^2$, is .333. The reader who is troubled by the notation can think of it this way: to calculate the variance of any variable, the weighted squared deviations of each value of the variable around the mean of the variable are summed and then divided by the sum of the weights. In this case the variable itself is a mean, but the procedure is the same. Each value of the variable is a mean, and the mean of the variable is, therefore, a mean of means.

These calculations show that if one drew a single random sample of size three from this population and used the sample mean, $\bar{x}$, as an estimator of the population mean, $\mu$, that, *on the average,* the sample mean is equal to the population mean. This follows because $\mu = 3$ and $\bar{x} = 3$. A glance at Table 13 shows that if any one sample were drawn, which would have to be one of the eighty-four, that the sample mean *may* or *may not* be equal to the population mean. It is only the mean of the means that is equal to the population mean.

The variance of the means was calculated as a measure of how close the means are to the population value. If it is impossible to draw a sample and have the sample mean to be exactly equal to the population mean, one would at least like to be "close," even though incorrect.

Would using the median of the sample rather than the mean bring better results? To answer this question the eighty-four sample medians have been arranged in a frequency distribution shown in Table 13. The distribution of medians is also symmetrical about the value 3.00. Calculation of the mean of the medians is 250.00/84 = 3.00. It is seen, then, that, if one used the sample median to estimate the population mean, $\mu$,

TABLE 13

FREQUENCY DISTRIBUTION OF MEDIANS
FOR
SAMPLES OF SIZE THREE

| Medians(Md) | f | f(Md) | f(Md)² |
|---|---|---|---|
| 4.25 | 1 | 4.25 | 18.0625 |
| 4.00 | 12 | 48.00 | 192.0000 |
| 3.75 | 6 | 22.50 | 84.3750 |
| 3.25 | 9 | 29.25 | 95.0625 |
| 3.00 | 28 | 84.00 | 252.0000 |
| 2.75 | 9 | 24.75 | 68.0625 |
| 2.25 | 6 | 13.50 | 30.3750 |
| 2.00 | 12 | 24.00 | 48.0000 |
| 1.75 | 1 | 1.75 | 3.0625 |
| | 84 | 252.00 | 790.0000 |

that, *on the average,* the sample median is equal to $\mu$. The variance of the sample medians is calculated as:

$$S^2_{Md} = \frac{\Sigma f_i(Md_i - \overline{Md})^2}{84} = \frac{\Sigma f(Md)^2}{84} - \overline{Md}^2$$

$$= \frac{2891.000}{84} - 3^2$$

$$= 9.405 - 9$$

$$= .405$$

The variance of the sample medians, $S^2_{Md}$, is .405 which is larger than the variance of the sample means. This is interpreted as meaning that the sample medians are more disperse or variable around the true value, $\mu = 3$, than the sample means are. Accepting the variance as a measure of "closeness" indicates that the median is not quite as good an estimator of $\mu$ as the sample mean is.

This is a general conclusion. The variance of the sample means is always less than (or equal in some cases) than the variance of the sample medians.

If one wanted to maximize his chances of being correct, the sample median would seem to be superior to the mean as an estimator of $\mu$. The sample median is exactly three in $^{28}\!/_{64} = 33\%$ of the samples, while the sample mean is equal to three in $^{18}\!/_{84} = 21\%$ of the samples. This is not a general result, however.

The distribution of sample medians appears somewhat peculiar, having three relative modes. This is due to the fact that interpolation was used, assuming each score was evenly distributed over an interval of size one according to the method shown in Chapter II. If the median is reported as the middle score which occurred in the sample, then the distribution of medians is:

| Md | $f$ |
|----|-----|
| 4  | 19  |
| 3  | 46  |
| 2  | 19  |

The variance of this distribution is .452, which is even larger than before. As the sample size increases, the apparent "peculiarity" of the distribution of sample medians disappears.

The third estimator of $\mu$ to be considered is the mid-range. The frequency distribution of sample mid-ranges is shown in Table 14.

TABLE 14

FREQUENCY DISTRIBUTION OF MID-RANGES
FOR
SAMPLES OF SIZE THREE

| Mid-range(Mr) | $f$ | $f(MR)$ | $f(MR)^2$ |
|---------------|-----|---------|-----------|
| 4.5 | 1 | 4.5 | 20.25 |
| 4.0 | 9 | 36.0 | 144.00 |
| 3.5 | 20 | 70.0 | 245.00 |
| 3.0 | 24 | 72.0 | 216.00 |
| 2.5 | 20 | 50.0 | 125.00 |
| 2.0 | 9 | 18.0 | 36.00 |
| 1.5 | 1 | 1.5 | 2.25 |
|     | 84 | 252.0 | 788.50 |

The mean of the mid-ranges is three and the variance of the mid-ranges is:

$$S_{MR}^2 = \frac{\Sigma f(MR)^2}{84} - \overline{MR}^2$$

$$= \frac{788.50}{84} - 3^2 = 9.388 - 9$$

$$= .388$$

The variance of the sample mid-ranges is again larger than the variance of means.

The general conclusions that can be drawn are these: (1) the mean, median and mid-range all share the property that, on the average, their value is equal to the population mean, $\mu$. This is defined as the property unbiasedness. As estimator, E, is said to be an unbiased estimator of $\mu$, if the mean of E calculated for all possible samples is equal to $\mu$. In symbols, $\overline{E} = \mu$; (2) the variance of the sample mean is less than (or equal) to the variance of both the variances of the median and mid-range. This property is called *efficiency*. An estimator, E, is called an *efficient* estimator of $\mu$ if for all unbiased estimators of $\mu$, E is the one which has minimum variance. The sample mean is both an unbiased and efficient estimator of $\mu$. Since the mean has these properties, in addition to others not discussed here, we shall be primarily interested in using the sample mean as a "guess" for the population mean.

A general formula which gives the variance of the sample mean is:

$$S_{\overline{X}}^2 = \frac{\sigma^2}{n}(1 - n/N)$$

To verify this formula for the distribution of means in Table 12, recall that $\sigma^2 = 1.5$, $n = 3$ and $N = 9$:

$$S_{\overline{X}}^2 = \frac{1.5}{3}(1 - 3/9) = .5(1 - 1/3) = .5(2/3)$$
$$= .333$$

which is identical to that calculated before. Some interesting facts can be seen from this formula. First, the quantity $n/N$ is called the sampling fraction. It is the proportion of the population which is included in any one sample. As the sampling fraction increases, the variance of the mean decreases. If $n = N$, or every unit in the population were sampled, then $S_{\overline{X}}^2 = 0$. This is as it should be for, in this case, the sample mean would be the population mean. Suppose that the sample size, n, is small relative to the population size, N. In this case the sampling fraction is near zero and the variance of the sample mean is simply $\sigma^2/n$. This leads to the conclusion that the variance of the mean is virtually independent of the population size, provided that the sampling fraction is small. For example, suppose two populations have the same variance, $\sigma^2$. The first population consists of $N_1 = 20,000$ units and the second population of $N_2 = 100,000$ units. Further, suppose a sample of $n = 100$ is drawn from each population. The variance of the sample mean for the first population as given by the formula is:

$$\frac{\sigma^2}{100}(1 - 100/20,000) = \frac{\sigma^2}{100}(1 - .005) = \frac{\sigma^2}{100}(.995) = .00995\,\sigma^2$$

The variance of the sample mean for the second population is:

$$\frac{\sigma^2}{100}(1 - 100/100{,}000) = \frac{\sigma^2}{100}(1 - .001) = \frac{\sigma^2}{100}(.999) = .00999\,\sigma^2$$

These two variances are almost identical. If we were sampling Stanford-Binet I.Q. scores which have a variance of about 256 (i.e. $\sigma^2 = 256$), then the two sample means would have variances of

$$.00995(256) = 2.547;$$
$$.00999(256) = 2.557.$$

Taking square roots, the standard deviations of the sample means are 1.596 and 1.599. The two sample means have equal precision for all practical purposes.

   To summarize, if the sampling fraction is small, then the population size is of little consequence. Even if one population is very much larger than another population, samples of equivalent sizes from each will result in sample means of virtually equal variance or precision. This fact does not seem "intuitively reasonable" to the average person, but it is true, nevertheless.

   The net result is: for large populations, the variance of the mean is $\frac{\sigma^2}{n}$ (assuming the population is normal). For comparison purposes, the variance of the median is $\pi\sigma^2/2n$. The ratio of these two variances is

$$\frac{\sigma^2}{n} \bigg/ \frac{\pi\sigma^2}{2n} = 1 \bigg/ \frac{\pi}{2} = 2 \bigg/ \pi = .637$$

This is interpreted to mean that the median is only 64% as efficient as the mean. The mean, based on a sample of size 64 would give the same variance as the median based on 100 observations. Statisticians base their judgment upon considerations such as this to determine what particular statistics to use for what particular problems.


## Sample Estimators of a Population Variance

   The sampling distribution of the mean has been studied, and it was concluded that the sample mean was both an unbiased and an efficient estimator of the population mean. In this section estimates of the population variance will be considered. The motivation is two-fold: (1) interest is in the variance as a description of the population, and, (2) since the variance of the sample mean has been seen as a direct function of the population variance, an estimate of the population variance is necessary in order to interpret the sample mean.

Only one estimator will be presented. This is the sample variance, $S^2$, with one modification. The weighted sums of squares about the mean will be divided by n–1 rather than n (as was done with the population variance). The defining formula and its equivalent are:

$$S^2 = \frac{\Sigma f_i (x_i - \bar{x})^2}{n-1} = \frac{\Sigma f x^2}{n-1} - \frac{(\Sigma f x)^2}{n(n-1)}$$

The individual eighty-four sample variances were calculated from the samples of size three in the foregoing section and are summarized in Table 15. Note that the distribution of sample variances is positively skewed.

TABLE 15

FREQUENCY DISTRIBUTION OF VARIANCES
FOR
SAMPLES OF SIZE THREE

| Variance($S^2$) | $f$ | $f(S^2)$ |
|---|---|---|
| 4.3333 | 4 | 17.3332 |
| 4.0000 | 3 | 12.0000 |
| 3.0000 | 2 | 6.0000 |
| 2.3333 | 20 | 46.6660 |
| 1.3333 | 10 | 13.3330 |
| 1.0000 | 24 | 24.0000 |
| .3333 | 20 | 6.6660 |
| .0000 | 1 | .0000 |
| | 84 | 125.9982 |

The mean of variances is calculated by weighting each value by the corresponding frequency and is:

$$\bar{S}^2 = \frac{\Sigma f S^2}{84} = \frac{125.9982}{84} = 1.4999$$

Recall that the population variance, $\sigma^2$, was 1.5. The sample variance, $S^2$, is seen to be an unbiased estimator of $\sigma^2$ (apart from rounding error).

If $S^2$ for $\sigma^2$ is substituted in the formula for the variance of the mean, then an unbiased *estimate* of the variance of a sample mean is:

$$S_{\bar{X}}^2 = \frac{S^2}{n} (1 - n/N)$$

and, if the population size is sufficiently large relative to the sample size, then it is:

$$S_{\bar{X}}^2 = S^2/n$$

One might be inclined to estimate the population standard deviation by merely taking the square root of $S^2$, the estimate of the variance. In Table 16 the frequency distribution of the eighty-four standard deviations calculated by taking square roots of the variances are shown. The mean of this distribution is:

$$\bar{S} = \Sigma fS/84 = 95.392/84 = 1.136$$

TABLE 16

FREQUENCY DISTRIBUTION OF STANDARD DEVIATIONS
FOR
SAMPLES OF SIZE THREE

| Standard Deviations(S) | f | fS |
|:---:|:---:|:---:|
| 2.082 | 4 | 8.328 |
| 2.000 | 3 | 6.000 |
| 1.732 | 2 | 3.464 |
| 1.528 | 20 | 30.560 |
| 1.150 | 10 | 11.500 |
| 1.000 | 24 | 24.000 |
| .577 | 20 | 11.540 |
| 0 | 1 | 0 |
| | 84 | 95.392 |

The population standard deviation is $\sigma = \sqrt{1.5} = 1.225$. The fact is that even though $S^2$ is an unbiased estimator of $\sigma^2$, S is a *biased* estimator of $\sigma$. This bias is small enough to be neglected for practical purposes and tends to disappear as n becomes large. The standard deviation of the mean is estimated, then, by using $S_{\bar{x}} = S/\sqrt{n}$ even though there may be a slight bias.

Other estimators of $\sigma^2$ are available, but $S^2$ is the most efficient.

# CHAPTER V

# Statistical Inference

## Confidence Intervals

As shown, if a sample of n observations is taken from some population having a mean, $\mu$, and variance, $\sigma^2$, that the sample mean, $\bar{X}$, and sample variance, $S^2$, are unbiased and efficient estimators of $\mu$ and $\sigma^2$. Also available is an estimate of the variance of the sample mean, i.e. $S^2/n$.

The interesting feature of a *point estimate,* such as a sample mean, is that few people believe it to be correct! Suppose one takes a sample of fifty observations from some large population. A "best" estimate or a "good guess" of the population mean is desired. Fortified with the knowledge that the sample mean, $\bar{X}$, is a good estimate, one calculates $\bar{X}$ to be, say, 104. This is the estimate of $\mu$ that is reported, but it is realized that $\mu$ could be 105 or 100 or 104.8. By inspecting the sampling distribution of means in Table 12, this idea gets support. In Table 12 only 21% of the sample means are equal to the population mean. This means that the odds are roughly 3.5 to 1 that a sample will be drawn for which the sample mean is *not* equal to the population mean. As the number of possible values of the random variable increase, the probability of obtaining an $\bar{X}$ equal to $\mu$ tends to decrease. For continuous random variables, where an infinity of values of x are possible, the probability that a sample $\bar{X}$ equals the population mean, $\mu$, is zero. The net result of all this is the somewhat paradoxical fact that even though $\bar{X}$ is a "best" estimate of $\mu$, it is unlikely that a particular sample mean will equal $\mu$.

It seems, then, that when a particular value is reported as an estimate, one ought to supplement it with some measure of how far from $\mu$ the estimate might be. The answer is how far it *might* be is: it might be any distance away—at least as far as the upper limit or lower limit of the variable. What can be said, however, is how far from $\mu$ the sample estimate is likely to be. Therefore, there are two considerations: (1) some measure of distance, and (2) some measure of probability.

Suppose, for the moment, that we knew $\sigma^2$ was 1.5, as we did for the population of nine numbers in Table 10. We calculated the variance of the mean for samples of size three to be .333. The standard deviation is $\sqrt{.333} = .577$. From Chebyshev's inequality we could then calculate a lower bound for the probability that a sample mean would be within "k" standard deviations of the population mean. Referring to Table 9 we see that the probability is at least .75 that $\bar{x}$ will be within two standard deviations of the mean. Two standard deviations is 2(.577) or 1.154. It is known, then, that whatever $\mu$ is, the sample mean will be between $\mu - 1.154$ and $\mu + 1.154$ with a probability of at least .75. Now suppose that we obtain a particular $\bar{x}$. We could calculate $\bar{x} - 1.154$ and $\bar{x} + 1.154$ giving us a lower and an upper value. Would these lower and upper values bracket or contain the true value, $\mu$? Yes, if the obtained $\bar{x}$ is one of the 75% that we know are within 1.154 standard deviations of $\mu$. No, if the obtained $\bar{x}$ is one of those outside 1.154 standard deviations of $\mu$.

If we repeatedly sampled from the population, each time obtaining an $\bar{x}$, and each time calculating $\bar{x} - 1.154$ and $\bar{x} + 1.154$, then at least 75% of these limits would bracket $\mu$. On the scale of x below is indicated the population mean, $\mu$, and intervals around observed sample means.

Sample means, a, d, and e are close enough to $\mu$ so that adding and subtracting 1.154 results in ranges of values, which cover or contain $\mu$. These three means are part of the 75%, which are that close to $\mu$. Sample means, b, c and f are "far" from $\mu$ so that their intervals do not cover $\mu$. These three means are not part of the 75% "close" to $\mu$.

In any particular problem only one sample is taken. Only one $\bar{x}$ is calculated, and only one interval obtained. Does this interval contain $\mu$? There is no way to tell, but we can say that we are at least seventy-five percent "confident" that $\mu$ is within the obtained interval. For example, if the standard deviation of the mean is .577 and a sample mean of 8 is observed, then we could say we are at least .75 confident that $\mu$ is between $8 - 1.154$ and $8 + 1.154$, or 6.846 and 9.154. If a narrower interval is desired, then our confidence that $\mu$ is in this interval decreases. For example, the lower bound for the probability that $\bar{x}$ will be within 1.5 standard deviations of the mean is .56 (from Table 8). Consequently, the interval, $8 - 1.5(.577)$ to $8 + 1.5(.577)$, or 7.134 to 8.866, covers $\mu$ with confidence being at least .56. The amount of "confidence" can range between zero and one, and is called the confidence coefficient.

Before the particular sample is taken, the *probability* that an interval with confidence coefficient, C, will include the true value is equal to C. After the sample is taken and a particular interval obtained, the probability is either zero or one. This is because the interval either contains $\mu$ or it does not. The population mean, $\mu$, is *not* a random variable. It is a fixed number for a particular population. Since probability is only defined for random variables, it would be incorrect to say that the probability that $\mu$ is between 6.846 and 9.154 is .75. To put it another way, the random feature of a *confidence interval* is the limits. The sample is random, $\bar{x}$ is random, and, therefore, the limits are random. Probability can be applied to the limits before the sample is taken. After the sample is taken, there is no longer any doubt about the limits. They are observed to be two numbers. It is analogous to saying that the probability of throwing a four on a six-sided die is $\frac{1}{6}$. After the die is thrown and four is observed, there is no probability statement referring to the number four. It is an observed fact.

After the limits are observed, there still is doubt about $\mu$, but since $\mu$ is a fixed number with no probability distribution, a statement concerning the probability of $\mu$ is improper. The word, confidence, is substituted instead. The definition of this word is not at all clear. Many authors of statistical text-books completely sidestep the issue by leaving the term undefined or by appealing to the reader's intuition. Freeman[1] says, ". . . it is evident that unless some such relative frequency interpretation of the interval constructed from the data of a particular problem is tolerated, confidence interval theory can have little useful application." The so-called Bayesian statisticians interpret these intervals somewhat differently, but more of that later.

Using the theory of confidence intervals, goals—both of finding a

---

[1] Harold Freeman, *Introduction to Statistical Inference,* (Reading, Mass.: Addison-Wesley, 1963) p. 309.

measure of distance and of finding a measure of confidence—have been accomplished. The approach taken has been conservative in the sense that the confidence coefficients (.75, .56, etc.) were only lower bounds as given by the Chebyshev inequality. In Table 12 it is seen that $^{82}/_{84} =$ 97.6% of the means are between $3 - 1.154 = 1.846$ and $3 + 1.154 = 4.154$. Sampling from this population would allow one to either raise our confidence coefficient from .75 to .976 or to keep .75 (but narrow the limits). The difficulty is: one does not know that this is the population. If it were known, we wouldn't be sampling.

However, there is a very strong statement to be made about the distribution of sample means. This statement is one form of the central limit theorem. The theorem states that if the population has a mean and variance that the distribution of sample means tends toward normality, as the sample size becomes large. The power behind this theorem is that the population need *not* have any particular form of distribution. Much work has been done investigating how large the sample must be in order for the theorem to take effect. Suffice it to say, that samples of as low as ten to fifteen are sufficient for practical purposes, if the population is bell-shaped and symmetrical. Samples of thirty to fifty are sufficient for most other populations except, perhaps, for extremely skewed populations. If the population is normal, then the distribution of sample means is normal for any size of sample.

This theorem allows one to refer to the table of the normal distribution in order to find the confidence coefficient for a given interval length. This, of course, results in much stronger statements than what the Chebyshev inequality would allow. For example the confidence interval, $\bar{x} - 2(.577)$ to $\bar{x} + 2(.577)$ or $\bar{x} - 1.154$ to $\bar{x} - 1.154$, is a .95 confidence interval, since the probability of a sample mean being within two standard deviations of the mean assuming normality is .95. The actual value of z is 1.96, but we have rounded off to 2 for convenience. (See Table 9.)

As observed earlier, we seldom know the population variance, $\sigma^2$. Hence, we usually cannot calculate the standard deviation of the mean, $\sigma/\sqrt{n}$. The estimator $S/\sqrt{n}$, where S is the standard deviation calculated from the sample of n, is slightly biased, but the bias is small and can be ignored. However, using $S/\sqrt{n}$ as an estimator of $\sigma/\sqrt{n}$ introduces another source of random variation into the confidence limits. Previously, the only element which occurred by chance was $\bar{x}$. In addition, we now have S, and $S/\sqrt{N}$, occurring by chance. It seems intuitively obvious that the confidence coefficients, using both estimates, x̄ and $S/\sqrt{N}$, would be expected to be different from that obtained if only x̄ is used. This is true. Since an additional source of error is being admitted, the confidence coefficient for a given number of standard deviations decreases. An English scientist, writing under the pen-name of Student in 1908, gave the derivation of the probability distribution used for the above problem. Today, we call this distribution Student's "t" distribution or simply, the t distribution. The t distribution is symmetrical about $t = 0$ and is bell-shaped. To many people it appears almost "normal," but it differs in the sense that the distribution of probability (or total area) is not as concentrated around the mean as it is for the normal distribution. A given percentile rank occurs further from the mean of the t distribution (relative to the scale of t) than it does in a normal distribution (relative to the z scale). This means there is less area between any two points around the mean under the t curve than between the same two points under the normal curve. Consequently, either the confidence coefficients must decrease or the intervals lengthened in order to keep the same confidence.

The normal distribution has two parameters, $\mu$ and $\sigma^2$, while the t distribution has only one. This single parameter is called degrees of freedom and relates to the number of restrictions imposed on the sample. In the present case with a sample of size n, there are $n - 1$ degrees of freedom. The z transformation of the normal distribution allows one to use one table for all normal distributions, since the relative areas under all normal curves between any two z values are the same. The t curve changes its relative shape each time the degrees of freedom, $n - 1$, changes. The table of the t distribution, then, must be entered with the parameter, degrees of freedom. The upper .05, .025, .01 and .005 points of the t distribution are shown in Table 17. Note that the first column contains values of "df" which means degrees of freedom. Entering the table with 18 degrees of freedom, the upper .05 point is read as 1.734. This means 95% of the area under a t curve with 18 degrees of freedom is below 1.734. Also, the value of t which includes .95 of the area beween $-t$ and $+t$ is 2.101 (with 18 df), because .025 is above 2.101 and, therefore, .025 is below $-2.101$ because of symmetry.

Going down the first column brings one to the entry "∞." This symbol means "infinite" degrees of freedom. Comparing the entries in the t table

## TABLE 17

UPPER PERCENTAGE POINTS OF THE T DISTRIBUTION

| d.f. | .05 | .025 | .01 | .005 |
|------|-----|------|-----|------|
| 1 | 6.314 | 12.706 | 31.821 | 63.657 |
| 2 | 2.920 | 4.303 | 6.965 | 9.925 |
| 3 | 2.353 | 3.182 | 4.541 | 5.841 |
| 4 | 2.132 | 2.776 | 3.747 | 4.604 |
| 5 | 2.015 | 2.571 | 3.365 | 4.032 |
| 6 | 1.943 | 2.447 | 3.143 | 3.707 |
| 7 | 1.895 | 2.365 | 2.998 | 3.500 |
| 8 | 1.860 | 2.306 | 2.897 | 3.355 |
| 9 | 1.833 | 2.262 | 2.821 | 3.250 |
| 10 | 1.813 | 2.228 | 2.764 | 3.169 |
| 11 | 1.796 | 2.201 | 2.718 | 3.106 |
| 12 | 1.782 | 2.179 | 2.681 | 3.055 |
| 13 | 1.771 | 2.160 | 2.650 | 3.012 |
| 14 | 1.761 | 2.145 | 2.625 | 2.977 |
| 15 | 1.753 | 2.132 | 2.603 | 2.947 |
| 16 | 1.746 | 2.120 | 2.584 | 2.921 |
| 17 | 1.740 | 2.110 | 2.567 | 2.898 |
| 18 | 1.734 | 2.101 | 2.552 | 2.878 |
| 19 | 1.729 | 2.093 | 2.540 | 2.861 |
| 20 | 1.725 | 2.086 | 2.528 | 2.845 |
| 21 | 1.721 | 2.080 | 2.518 | 2.831 |
| 22 | 1.717 | 2.074 | 2.508 | 2.819 |
| 23 | 1.714 | 2.069 | 2.500 | 2.807 |
| 24 | 1.711 | 2.064 | 2.492 | 2.787 |
| 25 | 1.708 | 2.060 | 2.485 | 2.787 |
| 26 | 1.706 | 2.056 | 2.479 | 2.779 |
| 27 | 1.703 | 2.052 | 2.473 | 2.771 |
| 28 | 1.701 | 2.048 | 2.467 | 2.763 |
| 29 | 1.699 | 2.045 | 2.462 | 2.756 |
| 30 | 1.697 | 2.042 | 2.457 | 2.750 |
| 40 | 1.684 | 2.021 | 2.423 | 2.705 |
| 50 | 1.676 | 2.009 | 2.403 | 2.678 |
| 60 | 1.671 | 2.000 | 2.390 | 2.660 |
| 80 | 1.664 | 1.990 | 2.374 | 2.639 |
| 100 | 1.660 | 1.984 | 2.364 | 2.626 |
| ∞ | 1.645 | 1.960 | 2.326 | 2.576 |

Reprinted from D. B. Owens, *Handbook of Statistical Tables* (Reading, Mass.: Addison-Wesley Inc., 1962), p. 28. By permission of the author and publishers.

for this line with the corresponding percentiles of the normal distribution, one will note they are the same. For example, 1.96 is the upper .025 point of both the t distribution and the normal distribution.

If, then, a sample of n = 25 was taken and $\bar{x}$ and $S/\sqrt{n}$ calculated, the .95 confidence interval for $\mu$ is calculated as

$$\bar{x} - t_{.025}\ S/\sqrt{n} < \mu < \bar{x} + t_{.025}\ S/\sqrt{n}$$

or

$$\bar{x} - (2.064)\ S/\sqrt{n} < \mu < \bar{x} + (2.064)\ S/\sqrt{n}$$

since t = 2.064 is the upper .025 point with 24 degrees of freedom. Suppose $\bar{x} = 102$ and S = 10.
Then,

$$102 - (2.064)(10)/\sqrt{25} < \mu < 102 + (2.064)(10)/\sqrt{25}$$
$$102 - 4.13 < \mu < 102 + .413$$
$$97.87 < \mu < 106.13$$

This is the .95 confidence interval for the population mean, $\mu$. If the sample size is large (over thirty), then the normal distribution could be used with little error. Note in the above example with n = 25, the correct value is t = 2.064 while the normal distribution gives z = 1.96.

A summary of when the various probability distributions apply is given below. The cell containing "?" requires special methods and will not be discussed here.

### $\sigma$ known

|  | population normal | not normal |
|---|---|---|
| small n | normal | Chebyshev |
| large n | normal | normal |

### $\sigma$ unknown

|  | population normal | not normal |
|---|---|---|
| small n | t | ? |
| large n | t or normal | t or normal |

## Statistical Tests of Hypotheses

An introduction to the theory of estimation was presented in the preceding section of this chapter. A closely related topic is the theory of testing hypotheses. While certain conclusions and decisions may result from the application of estimation techniques, the major emphasis of the theory of estimation is the statistical description of a population. The theory of testing hypotheses treats, explicitly, the problem of deciding between two mutually exclusive statements regarding a population.

A classical example of a test hypothesis was given by Fisher.[2] A lady claims that, by tasting a cup of tea, she can tell which of two ingredients, tea and milk, was added first to the cup. This assertion made by the lady suggests two hypotheses: that the lady cannot discriminate between these two types of cups of tea and second, that she can. The first hypothesis is called the *null* hypothesis, since it asserts the absence of an effect. The null hypothesis is usually symbollized by $H_0$. The second hypothesis is called the *alternative* hypothesis and is symbollized by $H_1$. Fisher suggests an experiment consisting of eight cups of tea—four prepared one way and four prepared the other way—which are presented to the lady in random order. The lady is requested to divide the cups into the original two groups of four. The method by which it is decided whether to reject $H_0$ or not is known as a *test of significance*.

The essential idea is to compare the results of the experiment with what could reasonably be expected by chance, if the lady actually had no power of discriminating between the two types of cups. The variable of interest here is x, the number of cups correctly classified. The probability distribution of x, assuming that only chance is operating, can be generated, using the theory of combinations, or, by enumerating all possible divisions of the eight cups into two groups of four, each time recording the value of x. There are seventy possible divisions distributed over the values of x, as shown below. The calculations leading to this distribution will not be shown, but note that odd values of x are impossible. The mis-classification of any one cup in a particular group results in another cup being mis-classified in the other group.

---

[2] R. A. Fisher, *The Design of Experiments* (New York: Hafner, 1960), p. 11.

| $x$ | Relative frequency | Probability |
|---|---|---|
| 8 | $\frac{1}{70}$ | .0143 |
| 6 | $\frac{16}{70}$ | .2286 |
| 4 | $\frac{36}{70}$ | .5143 |
| 2 | $\frac{16}{70}$ | .2286 |
| 0 | $\frac{1}{70}$ | .0143 |

It can be seen that it is fairly likely that, if $H_0$ is true, the lady would correctly classify 2, 4 or 6 cups (68 ways out of 70). It is unlikely that the lady would correctly classify 0 or 8 cups, if $H_0$ is true. If she did, indeed, classify no cups correctly, this would certainly not be evidence against $H_0$. Such a poor showing would be surprising and might even require further inquiry, but the fact remains that one certainly would not conclude that the lady could correctly discriminate between the two types of cups. If she correctly classifies all eight cups, however, we may reason as follows: if $H_0$ is true, then the probability of the lady scoring $x = 8$ is small (.0143). In other words, this result could not "reasonably" be expected by chance; some effect other than chance must be operating. The only effect we can identify is that claimed by the lady. Hence, $H_0$ is rejected and $H_1$ is accepted.

Three important questions are:

A. Is it possible that effects other than that claimed by the lady could influence the results?
B. How small must the probability of an event be in order to claim that the event is not expected by chance?
C. Is it possible that we could be incorrect when we reject $H_0$ even if no other effects are possible?

The answers to these questions, together with the probability distribution of $x$, form the very basis of the logic of a test of significance. The essential idea is: in a test of significance the chance distribution assuming $H_0$ is true, called the randomization distribution, is compared with one observation from a "randomization plus other effects" distribution. The randomization distribution given above is the distribution calculated under no other assumption but the haphazard arrangement of the eight cups into two groups of four. If other effects *are* operating—in particular if the lady can discriminate—then some other distribution would result. If $H_1$ is true, then it would be expected that the probability of observing $x = 8$ would be higher. If we agreed to reject $H_0$ in favor of $H_1$, if $x = 8$ is observed, then we are, in effect, stating that this observation is *prob-*

*ably not* from the pure randomization distribution, but from some other distribution—the "randomization plus effects" distribution. If only pure chance were operating, then the result, x = 8, could happen. Its probability is .0143, and, therefore, the probability that we incorrectly reject $H_0$, when in fact $H_0$ is true, (i.e. only randomization being operative), is .0143. This probability of error is conventionally called the *level of significance* and will be symbollized by £.

The level of significance is partially the experimenter's choice. If a higher probability of error can be tolerated, then the experimenter could decide to reject $H_0$ if x = 6 or 8. In this case £ would be .0143 + .2286 = .2429. The extreme case would be the decision to reject $H_0$ no matter what value of x was observed, in which case £ would be 1. The major criticism of this procedure would be not that a high risk of error were selected, but that it would be a waste of time to perform the experiment! At the other extreme, one could decide never to reject $H_0$, in which case £ = 0, but again the collection of data would be unnecessary. The level of significance, then, is selected somewhere between 0 and 1 and usually closer to zero in order to avoid making errors. Conventionally, £ is chosen near .01 or .05, but the actual choice should be dictated by the purpose of the particular experiment and the possible consequences of making this type of error.

The answer to question A posed above is, "yes," but given adequate experimental techniques and the mechanism of randomization we can hope to nullify or at least statistically control these extraneous effects. Suppose the lady were permitted to see us preparing the cups. She might perform very well, not because her ability to discriminate between the two types of prepared tea, but because of the effect of poor experimental technique. Extraneous effects, such as these, must be eliminated by good experimental methods. A different type of extraneous effect can arise in the following manner. Suppose four of the cups have slightly rougher edges than the other four, and suppose further that these four "rough" cups are exactly the cups chosen to receive the "milk first" preparation. The lady could receive a sensation from the "rough" edges, which she confuses with her supposed "milk first" sensation. She might then classify all eight cups correctly—not on the basis of a true ability to discriminate, but on the basis of differences among the cups. The way one controls this type of effect is to deliberately introduce chance into the experiment. This is done by randomly choosing the four cups to receive the "milk first" preparation. The point being that the probability of the four "rough" cups receiving the "milk first" preparation is equal to the probability of the lady correctly identifying the four "milk first" cups by chance alone! This probability is the significance level—in this case, .0143. When it is stated that the probability of correctly discriminating all eight cups by chance alone is .0143, we are not merely thinking of the lady being lucky, but also of the chance that when we randomize the preparations among the cups, that four cups of one type will all receive the same preparation.

The reader may have wondered why the experiment couldn't have been designed to nullify the "rough edge" effect, rather than leave it to chance. One reason could be that the experimenter is unaware of this effect. It might never have occurred to him that the cups were different in this respect. Suppose, however, that the experimenter *was* aware of this difference. He could have separated the cups into two groups— "rough" and "not rough." He could then randomly choose half of the "rough" cups to receive milk first and half to receive tea first. He could also randomize within the "not rough" group. This last act of randomization might seem unnecessary, since the experiment was designed to nullify the "rough-not-rough" effect. This is not so. The cups may have differed in some other way—perhaps in their thickness. Randomization could provide statistical control by deliberately introducing a chance element into the experiment so that a valid test of significance might be performed.

Applying these ideas to an educational experiment requires that the subjects serving as the experimental units, be randomly assigned to the experimental treatments. For example, one might want to compare two different types of programmed materials relative to how well students can learn a certain task. The students in the experimental group could be assigned randomly to one or the other of two programmed materials. These students differ in a countless number of ways, but the device of randomization provides the basis for a test of significance. First the students could be separated into "high I.Q." and "low I.Q." (analogous to the rough and not-rough cups). One could still randomize within the I.Q. groups, thereby statistically controlling factors such as socioeconomic level.

The reader may have heard the phrase, "Control all factors except the one under test." This canon of experimentation was, and still is, repeated by many people doing experimentation. While it may be desirable to do this, the fact of the matter is that it is impossible! R. A. Fisher showed the way to live with this impossibility—in the use of the device called randomization.

Another example of a test of significance is one used to test an hypothesis concerning a population mean, $\mu$. Suppose a fair amount of empirical research had been conducted with children having I.Q.'s in a range from 91 to 105, and it was consistently demonstrated that XYZ = reading test scores were related to I.Q. scores as shown in the following table.

| I.Q. | 91–95 | 96–100 | 101–105 |
|---|---|---|---|
| mean XYZ = score | 20 | 28 | 36 |

It is evident that, for the I.Q. range studied, the mean XYZ = reading score increases by eight points for every five point rise in I.Q. A research worker in this field might question if this relationship between I.Q. and reading scores would continue to hold for children with above average I.Q.'s. Specifically his interest is in children with I.Q.'s between 111 and 115. Since this I.Q. range is two steps above that shown in the table, he would expect the mean reading score for these children to be 52, if the relationship holds. Translated into a statistical hypothesis this becomes: $H_0 : \mu = 52$. That is, the null hypothesis is: the mean of the reading scores is 52, for students with I.Q.'s between 111 and 115. The alternative hypothesis is $H_1 : \mu \neq 52$ or that the mean reading score is not 52. It may be that $\mu$ is greater than 52 ($\mu > 52$) or that $\mu$ is less than 52 ($\mu < 52$). In either case, the relationship, as implied by the table, would not be the same for children of above average I.Q.'s. Consequently, $H_0$ should be rejected in either case.

The test of significance involves the sample mean, $\bar{x}$. It was seen earlier that the sampling distribution of sample means from a large population tended toward a normal distribution with expected value, $\mu$, and variance, $\sigma^2/N$. If $H_0$ were true, and if the researcher took repeated samples of 25 children's reading scores from the population, each time calculating a sample mean, the means would be normally distributed with a mean of 52 and variance $\sigma^2/25$. If the variance were known, one could calculate the probability that any one sample mean would deviate from the population mean of 52 by various numbers of points. For the moment, assume that $\sigma^2 = 36$ (which might be found from the table of norms provided with the test). The variance of sample means is 36/25, and the standard deviation is $\sqrt{36}/\sqrt{25} = \frac{6}{5}$ or 1.2. Referring to the table of the normal distribution (Table 9), the probability of a particular $\bar{x}$ being within one standard deviation of the mean is .68. Therefore, if the population mean is 52, the probability of $\bar{x}$ being between 50.8 and 53.2 is .68.

Using the same logic as before, inquire as to what is a "reasonable" expectation if $\mu = 52$. This depends on the level of significance, £, which we choose. If £ is chosen as .05, we are stating that, if we observe a sample mean which has probability of .05 or less, assuming $H_0$ to be true, that this result is not expected merely by chance and that, instead, $H_0$ is not true.

Since very large *or* very small means would be evidence against $H_0$, the total probability of .05 is partitioned into two parts of .025. The shaded regions under the normal distribution below illustrates the division.

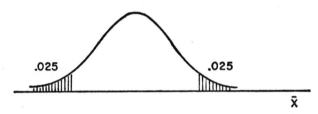

The mean test scores on the scale under the shaded areas is called the critical region.

The researcher takes a sample of twenty-five students and inspects whether or not it falls in the critical region. If it does, he states that $H_0$ is rejected or that $\mu$ is not 52. If it does not, then he fails to reject $H_0$ and states that his sample result is consistent with a population mean of 52.

The only problem remaining is to calculate how many standard deviations from $\mu$ the sample mean would have to be in order for it to fall in the critical region. Referring to Table 9 it is seen that the percentage of area between $z = -1.96$ and $z = 1.96$ is .95. The area outside these two values is .05. The rule is then: reject $H_0$ if $\bar{x}$ is more than 1.96 standard deviations from $\mu = 52$ (on either side).

If a mean of 56 were observed, then

$$z = \frac{\bar{x} - \mu}{\sigma/\sqrt{N}} = \frac{56-52}{1.2} = \frac{4}{1.2} = 3.3.$$

The sample mean is 3.3 standard deviations above 52. Therefore, the decision would be to reject $H_0$.

Again, it is realized that, when $H_0$ is rejected, an error may be committed. In fact, the theory states that five percent of the sample means would fall in the critical region when $H_0$ is true. The probability that any particular mean will be in the critical region giving that $H_0$ is true is .05. The probability of this type of error is thus .05.

There is another type of error, however, which can be made in a test of significance. Suppose the true population mean were 55. It could happen that a sample mean below 55 were observed, which did not fall in the critical region relative to the hypothesized mean of 52. In that case, the decision would be to fail to reject $H_0$ and an error would be committed. An example of this contingency is a sample mean of 54. If $\mu$ is actually 55, then a sample mean of 54 is not an unreasonable result. Calculating our test statistic for testing if $\mu = 52$ would give:

$$z = \frac{54-52}{1.2} = \frac{2}{1.2} = 1.67$$

Since 1.67 is between $-1.96$ and 1.96, it does not fall in the critical region, and, therefore, the decision would be to "fail to reject $H_0$." This is incorrect since $\mu$ was actually 55 and the decision was to fail to reject that hypothesis that $\mu = 52$.

This type of error is called the type two error, and its probability is symbollized by the Greek letter, $\beta$, (pronounced "beta"). To summarize, before the data is collected, there are two possible errors. The type one error is the error of rejecting $H_0$ when in fact $H_0$ is true, while the type two error is the error of failing to reject $H_0$ when in fact $H_0$ is false. The respective probabilities are given by $\pounds$ and $\beta$. After the data is collected and a decision made, only one of the two errors is possible. If the decision is to reject $H_0$, then either the decision was correct or the type one error was made. If the decision is to fail to reject $H_0$, then either the decision was correct or a type two error was committed. Suppose that $\mu_0$ is the value of $\mu$ specified by the null hypothesis and $\mu_1$ some other value of $\mu$ contained in the set of values represented by the alternative hypothesis.

The table below shows the four possibilities in any decision problem.

|  |  | Decision | |
|---|---|---|---|
|  |  | reject $H_0$ | fail to reject $H_0$ |
| Truth | $\mu_0$ | type one $\pounds$ | $1-\pounds$ |
|  | $\mu_1$ | $1-\beta$ | type two $\beta$ |

If $\mu_0$ is the true value of the mean, then with probabilities, £ and 1-£, the type one error or a correct decision is made. If $\mu_1$ is the true value, then with probabilities, 1-$\beta$ and $\beta$, a correct decision or the type two error is made. It seems, obvious that one would wish to minimize £ and $\beta$ and thereby maximize 1-£ and 1-$\beta$. For a fixed sample size, as £ decreases, it happens that $\beta$ increases. The extreme case mentioned earlier—that of setting £ to be zero—illustrates the point. If £ = 0, then we would never make the type one error, but we would never reject $H_0$ either. If $H_0$ is not true, then one would be certain to make the type two error. At the other extreme, we could set £ = 1, which would mean that we always reject $H_0$. If the null hypothesis were false, we would always detect that fact, since we always reject $H_0$. Therefore, $\beta = 0$, but, if the null hypothesis were true, we would always commit a type one error. The problem is to balance the two types of error so that neither is more serious than we would like. As mentioned previously, the type one error is conventionally set at .05 or .01. The type two error is often disregarded. A difficulty with the type two error is that it depends on the particular value of $\mu$ which is true. For testing $H_0 : \mu = 52$, $\beta$ would assume different values depending on whether $\mu$ were acually 55 or 58 for example.

The probability of the type two error decreases as the true value of $\mu$ is further and further away from the hypothesized value. This is intuitively appealing, since it should be easier to discriminate values which are more divergent than values which are "close." Because of this reason $\beta$ is usually thought of as a set of values rather than as one particular number.

One way to keep £ small and to simultaneously reduce $\beta$ is to increase the sample size, N. If more information is available upon which to base a decision, then fewer errors will be made. A research worker can specify what values of £ and $\beta$ are tolerable and then determine the sample size which would achieve this result. The routine application of tests of significance with £ always set at .05, and with little thought given to $\beta$, is poor statistical practice and should be discouraged.

Two tests of significance have been presented which are alike in several details. These are shown below.

|  | Tea-taster | Reading test |
|---|---|---|
| a. A null hypothesis | No ability to discriminate | $\mu = 52$ |

| | *Tea-taster* | *Reading test* |
|---|---|---|
| b. An alternative hypothesis | Ability | $\mu \neq 52$ |
| c. Type one error | .0134 | .05 |
| d. Test statistic | x = number correct | x̄ = sample mean (or z) |
| e. Sampling distribution | Randomization distribution | normal distribution |
| f. Critical region | x = 8 | z < − 1.96 and z > 1.96 |

g. Collection of data and calculation of test statistic

h. Comparison of statistic with critical region

In the reading test problem, it was assumed that the variance was known ($\sigma^2 = 36$). If the variance were not known, the sample variance, $S^2$, could be used as an estimate of $\sigma^2$. Recall from the previous section that when $S^2$ is used the probability distribution used is the "t" distribution. The test statistic would become $t = \dfrac{\bar{x} - \mu}{S/\sqrt{n}}$ which is distributed as the t-distribution with n–1 degrees of freedom (Table 17). The upper and lower .025 points of the t-distribution would be used to define the critical region (for $\pounds = .05$). If n = 25, then these points of the t-distribution with twenty-four degrees of freedom are −2.064 and 2.064. Consequently, the null hypothesis would be rejected if t < −2.064 or t > 2.064. The logic of the t-test is essentially the same as the test utilizing the normal distribution. The difference is that the sample is used to calculate both x̄ and $S^2$, and the t-distribution is used to define the critical region.

The reading test score problem led to what is referred to as a "two-tail" test of significance. The null hypothesis specified a single value of $\mu$ ($H_0 : \mu = 52$), and the alternative hypothesis specified values of $\mu$ both above and below that single value ($H_1 : \mu \neq 52$). The critical region was divided into two parts, each part having probability $\pounds/2$. The "upper tail" portion was used to detect values above 52, while the "lower tail" portion was used to detect values less than 52. The problems of the tea-tasting lady led to a "one-tail" test of significance. The null hypothesis is rejected only if the number of correct classifications are larger than what could reasonably be expected by chance. Hence, the critical region is wholly in the "upper tail" of the randomization distribution. Whether one should use a one or two-tail test depends on the particular problem.

The examples, discussed above, involved only single samples. A typical situation in educational experiments involves two samples, an experimental and a control group. For example, suppose a science teacher is investigating two different ways of teaching a certain unit. One method involves a "discovery" type approach in which the pupils are to experiment, with a minimum of supervision, in order to formulate various principles for themselves. Another method uses programmed materials which explain the various principles in an efficient manner, but does not require any "discovery" on the part of the students. The teacher feels the first method is better, but it requires a relatively longer time period in which to allow the pupils the freedom of following "blind alleys," hunches, etc. Consequently, the teacher wants to use the first method only if the pupils will learn more and retain more with the first method as compared with the second.

There are various ways to research this question in a school setting. One way consists of the teacher randomly splitting his class into two groups; having one group use method one, and one group use method two. A test or tests designed to measure whatever objectives the science teacher had in mind could be administered after the experiment. Perhaps later in the year tests could be administered again in order to measure retention or long term effects. The difficulty with this type of design is: it may be quite difficult administratively to split the two groups and keep them separate for the length of the unit. In addition, the pupils in one group might discuss their work with pupils in the other group and, consequently, the methods would, in a sense, be contaminated. The teacher might teach two sections of the same course. In one section he might use one method and in the other section, the other method. The difficulty with this design is that randomization of students would be lacking, and the statistical theory presented earlier would not apply. Educational experimentation in an ongoing school situation is no easy matter, but imaginative teachers and administrators can oftentimes plan realistic experiments, if a basic commitment to research is an accepted policy. (The author realizes that he may be discussing a very small percentage of schools.)

To continue with the example, suppose the two groups were selected, the experiment performed, and a test of the objectives administered. A statistical model could be formulated as follows. Let the scores of the students in the method one group be designated as $X_1, X_2, \ldots, X_{n_1}$, and let the scores of the students in the method two group be designated as $Y_1, Y_2, \ldots, Y_{n_2}$. That is, there are $n_1$ and $n_2$ students in groups one and two, respectively. We conceptualize the X scores as being a sample from a population normally distributed with a mean, $\mu_x$, and variance, $\sigma_x^2$. The Y scores are thought of as a sample from a population normally distributed with a mean, $\mu_y$, and variance, $\sigma_y^2$. The statistical hypothesis is that there is no difference in the means of the two populations or $H_0 : \mu_x = \mu_y$. The alternative hypothesis would be $H_1 : \mu_x \neq \mu_y$.

Fisher showed that under this model the statistic:

$$t = \frac{\bar{X} - \bar{Y}}{\sqrt{S^2 \left( \frac{1}{n_1} + \frac{1}{n_2} \right)}}$$

is distributed according to the t distribution with $n_1 + n_2 - 2$ degrees of freedom. The means of the two samples are $\bar{X}$ and $\bar{Y}$ and $S^2$ is a sample estimate of the population variance, $\sigma^2$, where it is assumed that $\sigma_x^2 = \sigma_y^2$. In other words, we have to assume that the variances of the two populations are equal. Two sample variances are calculated, one from the X scores, $S_x^2$, and one from the Y scores, $S_y^2$. Under the equality of variance assumption, these two sample estimates are estimating the same quantity. A "best" estimate would seem to be some sort of average of $S_x^2$ and $S_y^2$. Since more weight should be given to an estimate based on a larger sample, the result is that the $S^2$ in the above formula is a weighted average of the two sample variances, where the weights are the degrees of freedom, or:

$$S^2 = \frac{(n_1 - 1) S_x^2 + (n_2 - 1) S_y^2}{(n_1 - 1) + (n_2 - 1)}$$

$$= \frac{(n_1 - 1) S_x^2 + (n_2 - 1) S_y^2}{n_1 + n_2 - 2}$$

To illustrate the calculation, suppose:

$$\bar{X} = 48 \qquad\qquad \bar{Y} = 42$$
$$S_x^2 = 25 \qquad\qquad S_y^2 = 27$$
$$n_1 = 13 \qquad\qquad n_2 = 11$$

The over-all estimate of the variance is:

$$S^2 = \frac{(12)(25) + (10)(27)}{22}$$

$$= 25.9$$

Then $t = \dfrac{48 - 42}{\sqrt{(25.9)\left(\dfrac{1}{13} + \dfrac{1}{11}\right)}}$

$= \dfrac{6}{\sqrt{(25.9)(.077 + .091)}}$

$= \dfrac{6}{\sqrt{(25.9)(.168)}} = \dfrac{6}{\sqrt{4.35}}$

$= \dfrac{6}{2.09} = 2.87$

The observed $t = 2.87$. Using a level of significance of $\pounds = .05$ we want the upper and lower .025 points of the t-distribution with 22 degrees of freedom. Referring to Table 17 these are found to be $\pm 2.074$. Since the observed t is greater than 2.074 the null hypothesis of equality of means is rejected in favor of the alternative that $\mu_x \neq \mu_y$.

Confidence limits on the true difference, $\mu_x - \mu_y$, can also be calculated. The lower and upper .95 limits are:

$$(\bar{X} - \bar{Y}) \pm t_{.025} \sqrt{S^2(^1/n_1 + {}^1/n_2)}$$

or                              $6 \pm 2.074(2.09) = 6 \pm 4.3$

Then $C(1.7 < \mu_x - \mu_y < 10.3) = .95$

The interpretation of this confidence interval is that the difference in means is at least 1.7 points but probably not more than 10.3 points in favor of method one.

The net result is that the experiment shows evidence for the superiority of the discovery method. The statistical analysis merely says that the difference is more than a chance difference. That is, the difference is "statistically significant." Many people make the error of equating statistical significance with "practical significance." Regardless of whether the result is or is not a chance difference, the question remains as to whether a difference of means of up to ten points would justify the use of the more time-consuming discovery method. This is a question of practical significance and educational values. The answer is not to be found simply in a statistical analysis. When one reads various reports, one often sees the writers implying that since the observed difference is statistically significant, it is an important or "large" difference.

One further word about the two sample tests above, relative to the assumptions. Even though we assume normality and equality of variances, it happens that the t test is remarkably insensitive to minor departures from these assumptions. The t test is said to be "robust" to the assumptions—a most remarkable and important result.

There are numerous other tests of hypotheses. Some are for testing the equality of several means, variances, correlation coefficients, etc. Their basic logic is equivalent, however.

## Bayesian Statistical Inference

Two methods of making inferences about statistical parameters have been discussed—confidence interval estimation and tests of hypotheses. Confidence intervals provide a set of values for an unknown parameter which are "credible" or which are consistent with the statistical evidence. Tests of hypotheses furnish like statements in the sense that the statistical evidence is examined relative to a hypothesis concerning a set of values for a parameter or a statistical distribution. If the probability of the observed data is small, assuming the hypothesis is true, the hypothesis is rejected. The use of tests of hypotheses, with their focus on errors of rejecting or accepting hypotheses, is more in the spirit of decision making with resulting action to do or not do something, while the use of confidence intervals are more in the spirit of description.

Since science is more concerned with inferences rather than decisions, it seems that the use of confidence intervals is to be preferred, when the problem is one of scientific description. There are two difficulties with confidence intervals, however. The first concerns the interpretation of the obtained interval. If a .95 confidence interval is constructed for a population mean, $\mu$, after observing relevant data, it is said to be .95 confident that the limits of the interval contain $\mu$. The interpretation of ".95 confident" is: if we repeatedly sample from the population, 95% of the intervals will, indeed, contain $\mu$. It does not mean the particular interval obtained contains $\mu$ or that the probability is .95 that the interval contains $\mu$. This latter interpretation is one that people often make, but strictly speaking, is incorrect. The second difficulty is that the idea of "learning by experience" is not easily given expression in the construction of confidence intervals. If we have strong beliefs that certain values of the parameter are more credible than others before we collect the present data, it seems that the resulting interval should reflect those beliefs. These beliefs could well have resulted from a previous statistical calculation!

A method of inference, which directly deals with the above mentioned difficulties, is called Bayesian inference. Many of the ideas found in this theory are quite old, but the past decade or so has seen a renewal of interest in them, together with the development of new ideas. At present, statisticians are interested in developing Bayesian statistical methods principally due to Professor Leonard J. Savage's book,[3] published in 1954, which remains the basic reference work on this theory.

The distinguishing feature of this theory concerns the definition of probability. Probability has been defined by some to be a limit of a long-run frequency. There are philosophical objections to this definition (such as the existence of the limit and what is meant precisely by "long-run"). Since our purpose is merely to present the flavor of Bayesian statistics, details will not be discussed here. The Bayesian defines the probability of an event to be a measure of the degree of belief one has that the event will occur on the next trial. Since one person's degree of belief can differ from another's, this type of definition leads to a theory of what is called "subjective probability." Operationally, the probability of an event A, is such that the ratio of the probability that A will happen to the probability that A will not happen is the odds that one would just barely offer for A against not A. Symbollically,

$$\text{odds ratio} = \frac{P(A)}{P(\text{not }A)} = \frac{P(A)}{1-P(A)}$$

For example, suppose that a coin is picked at random from a bag of coins. What odds would you be willing to give that when the coin is flipped heads will occur on the next toss? Put another way, suppose I am willing to bet one dollar on "tails." How much would you be willing to pay me if "tails" does, indeed, appear, assuming you are making a fair wager *according to your belief?* If your response is one dollar, then

$$\text{odds ratio (head to tails)} = \frac{\$1}{\$1} = 1$$

$$\text{and } \frac{P(A)}{1-P(A)} = \frac{1}{1} = \frac{.50}{.50}$$

or $P(H)$, the probability of heads is .50.
If your response is $0.50, then

---

[3] Leonard J. Savage, *The Foundations of Statistics* (New York: John Wiley and Sons, 1954).

$$\text{odds ratio} = \frac{\$.50}{\$1} = \frac{1}{2}$$

$$\text{and } \frac{P(H)}{1-P(H)} = \frac{1}{2} = \frac{.33}{.67}$$

and your probability of heads is .33. (This assumes you are not trying to take advantage of me!)

The idea of subjective probability may seem strange, but it is quite close to how "probability" is referenced in folk-lore. Statements such as, "What is the probability that the sun will rise tomorrow?" or "It is likely that the type of early childhood training a person had is related to later adjustment" are common. This does not justify the concept of subjective probability, but these statements do illustrate how probability or credibility can be linked with a degree of belief.

Accepting the concept of degree of belief, the question arises as to how one determines his belief or how one specifies his odds ratio. The Bayesian assumes that for any individual, there is a unique distribution of belief. Oftentimes, as with the coin problem above, one is somewhat vague about his belief, and any odds different than 1 to 1 could not be offered with any confidence. If this is the case, then one has a distribution of belief which is characterized by an "indifference" distribution. The changing from indifference to confident beliefs is the subject of Bayesian inference. This purpose is not a strange one since the use of confidence intervals and tests of hypotheses have essentially the same purpose.

To illustrate the Bayesian method, let us consider an elementary problem in probability theory. Suppose there are two boxes of balls. The first box contains four white and six black balls. The second box contains seven white and three black balls. One of the boxes is chosen at random and a ball is drawn at random from the selected box. One might ask for the probability of obtaining a white ball. If the first box is drawn, the probability of a white ball is .4, and if the second box is drawn, the probability of a white ball is .7. These are called conditional probabilities, since they depend on the selection of the box. Symbolically, $P(W/1) = .4$, which is read, "The probability of a white ball given that box one is selected is .4." Similarly, $P(W/2) = .7$. The problem is the proper combination of these two probabilities in order to arrive at an over-all answer for $P(W)$, the probability of a white ball.

This is achieved by weighting these two numbers by the probabilities of selecting the first and second boxes, respectively. Then $P(W) = P(1)$

$P(W/1) + P(2) P(W/2)$. If it is equally likely that box one or box two is selected, then $P(W) = (.5) (.4) + (.5) (.7) = .55$. However, if box one has probability .75 of being selected, then $P(W) = (.75) (.4) + (.25) (.7) = .475$.

A somewhat more interesting question is, "If a white ball was drawn, what is the probability that it came from box one?" This is a question of inverse probability, since it deals with an antecedent condition after a certain outcome has occurred. This question can be answered by using Bayes' theorem from which Bayesian statistics derives its name.[4] The probability sought here is written as $P(1/W)$ or the probability of box one given that a white ball has been observed. Bayes' theorem states that

$$P(1|W) = \frac{P(1) P(W|1)}{P(W)} = \frac{P(1) P(W|1)}{P(1) P(W|1) + P(2) P(W|2)}$$

If the selection of the boxes were equally likely, then

$$P(1\ W) = \frac{(.5) (.4)}{(.5) (.4) + (.5) (.7)} = \frac{.20}{.55} = .367$$

The probability that the white ball came from box one is a little greater than one-third, or the odds are a little less than two to one that the white ball came from box two (i.e. .633/.637 or 1.7 to 1). If $P(1) = .75$, then $P(W) = .475$ and $P(1|W) = .300/.475$ or .63.

The probabilities, $P(1)$ and $P(2)$, are called *a priori* or prior probabilities, and $P(1|W)$ and $P(2|W)$ are called *a posteriori* or posterior probabilities, since they are "after the fact" of observing the white ball. For the problem above, the prior odds for box two versus box one were 1 to 1, but after observing a white ball, the odds are 1.7 to 1 that box two was chosen. It should be emphasized that Bayes' theorem is true and is not the subject of debate. What is argued is its application and the definition of the probabilities entering into it.

In science, one frequently meets opposing hypotheses or models which attempt to explain the same set of observed facts. These hypotheses can be thought of as the boxes in our problem. The observations of science can be thought of as the observation of a white ball being drawn from the box. The question is, then, "Given that we observed this data, what is the probability that hypothesis one is true?" The prior probabilities for the hypotheses, $P(H_1)$ and $P(H_2)$, would be measures of an individual scientist's (or a collection of scientists') degree of belief in the

---

[4] Named after the English clergyman and mathematician, Thomas Bayes (1702–1761).

truth of the two hypotheses before the current set of data was collected. The posterior probabilities, $P(H_1|X)$ and $P(H_2|X)$, are measures of the scientist's belief after the observation X.

An application of Bayes' theorem in education is using it in mental tests for classification of individuals. Suppose a test is designed to predict future performance in some field of study. Normative data had already been obtained showing the distribution of test scores for students belonging to three groups—successful, moderately successful, and unsuccessful. The following table summarizes this data.

|  | Score on Test | | |
|---|---|---|---|
|  | 0–10 | 11–19 | 20–25 |
| Successful | .10 | .20 | .70 |
| Moderately successful | .20 | .50 | .30 |
| Unsuccessful | .50 | .40 | .10 |

The table shows the proportions of each group who scored from 0 to 10, 11 to 19, and 20–25. Note that the proportions in each row sum to one. Since the proportions of each group are different from the various score categories, one can see that the test has some predictive validity.

Let "s" represent successful, "m" represent moderately successful and "u," unsuccessful. The relevant probabilities are $P(s|22)$, $P(m|22)$ and $P(u|22)$. That is, the counsellor wants estimates of the probabilities that this student will be successful, moderately successful, and unsuccessful given that the student scored 22. By Bayes' theorem,

$$P(s|22) = \frac{P(s)\ P(22|s)}{P(22)}$$

$$= \frac{P(s)\ P(22|s)}{P(s)\ P(22|s) + P(m)\ P(22|m) + P(u)\ P(22|u)}$$

This is of the same form as the box and ball problem. The "boxes" are now the three groups, and the test score is analogous to the drawing of a ball. The prior probabilities, $P(s)$, $P(m)$ and $P(u)$ represent the counsellor's degree of belief that this student belongs to the various groups. How does he assess these? First, he might have previous data on the proportion of students who were in this category. Second, he might have other data and impressions about this particular student which causes him to modify the proportions mentioned above. In fact, if these impressions were well-articulated, he could possibly have applied Bayes' theorem previously, and the resulting posterior probabilities would be the prior probabilities for the current set of data (i.e. the test score). If the proportions of past students in these three groups were .20, .30, and .50, and, if the counsellor had no other relevant impressions about this student, then:

$$P(s|22) = \frac{(.20)\ (.70)}{(.20)\ (.70) + (.30)\ (.30) + (.50)\ (.10)}$$

$$= \frac{.14}{.14 + .09 + .05} = \frac{.14}{.28} = .50$$

and $\quad P(m|22) = \frac{(.30)\ (.30)}{.28} = \frac{.09}{.28} = .32$

$$P(u|22) = \frac{(.50)\ (.10)}{.28} = \frac{.05}{.28} = .18$$

The posterior probabilities of group membership are .50, .32, .18 respectively. The prior odds were 4 to 1 against membership in the successful group (.80/.20), while the posterior odds are 1 to 1 (.50/.50). This example shows how information is used to change prior beliefs according to the Bayesian model.

The problem of estimating a mean of a population can also be handled by Bayesian methods. Suppose one wanted to estimate the mean I.Q. for a city school system. The non-Bayesian approach, discussed earlier, would consist of taking a sample from the specified population and calculating the sample mean, X. This mean together with confidence limits would provide a point and interval estimate for the population mean, $\mu$. These calculations are virtually independent of previous experience and knowledge. The Bayesian approach would start with consideration of the prior distribution of belief about $\mu$. This distribution would represent current opinion and would be based upon accumulated knowledge of the characteristics of the particular school system. Figure seven depicts a possible prior distribution for the mean I.Q. To simplify calculations, seven intervals of width five have been used. It can be seen that the largest accumulation of probability is in the intervals centered around $\mu = 100$ and 105. It is fairly certain that this school population is "average," but there is some feeling that this system may be somewhat above average.

The bar centered about 105 is twice as tall as the bar centered about 95. This is interpreted to mean that if one had to choose between these

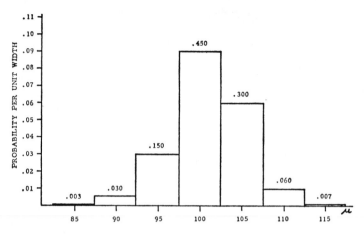

Figure 7. Prior Distribution for Mean I.Q.

two intervals, he would choose 102.5 to 107.5 and offer odds of two to one against $\mu$ being between 92.5 and 97.5. It is quite certain that $\mu$ is between 92.5 and 107.5. The total probability for this event is $.150 + .450 + .300 = .900$. *A priori,* one would say that $P(92.5 < \mu < 107.50) = .90$. This is similar to a confidence interval, except that it is constructed *before* the current set of data is collected and is based on our subjective belief.

If we take a sample of students and test them with the Stanford-Binet, we can assume $\sigma^2 = 256$. As before, we assume the distribution of the sample mean, X, is normally distributed with mean, $\mu$, and variance, $\sigma^2/n$. If sixteen students are sampled, the variance of the mean is $256/16 = 16$ and the standard deviation is 4. The z statistic $z = \dfrac{\bar{x} - \mu}{4}$ is normally distributed with a mean of zero and standard deviation of one.

After observing a particular $\bar{x}$, we want to calculate $P(\mu|\bar{x})$, the posterior probability of a value of $\mu$ given the observed result, $\bar{x}$. Since we are working with intervals, $P(\mu_i|\bar{x})$ will mean the probability of the $\mu$'s in the i[th] interval. Baye's theorem can be written as:

$$P(\mu_i|\bar{x}) = \frac{P(\mu_i)\ P(\bar{x}|\mu_i)}{\Sigma P(\mu_i)\ P(\bar{x}|\mu_i)}$$

Where $\mu_1, \mu_2, \ldots, \mu_7$ represent the seven intervals of $\mu$.

Since the $P(\mu_i)$ are known from the prior distribution, it is only necessary to calculate $P(\bar{x}|\mu_i)$. If $\bar{x}$ were observed to be 95, then $P(\bar{x} = 95|\mu_i)$ are the required numbers.

Table 18 displays the numbers used in the calculation of the posterior probabilities. Using the z statistic and $\bar{x} = 95$, the interval limits are converted to z scores. Referring to Table 9, which gives the probabilities

Table 18

CALCULATIONS FOR BAYES' THEOREM

| limits | z | $P(Z < z)$ | $P(x|\mu_1)$ | $P(\mu_1)$ | Product | $P(\mu_1|x)$ |
|--------|-----|-----------|-----------|-----------|---------|-----------|
| 117.5 | −5.625 | .000 | | | | |
| | | | .000 | .007 | .000 | .000 |
| 112.5 | −4.375 | 000 | | | | |
| | | | .000 | .060 | .000 | .000 |
| 107.5 | −3.125 | .000 | | | | |
| | | | .030 | .300 | .009 | .047 |
| 102.5 | −1.875 | .030 | | | | |
| | | | .236 | .450 | .106 | .552 |
| 97.5 | − 6.25 | .266 | | | | |
| | | | .468 | .150 | .070 | .365 |
| 92.5 | 6.25 | .734 | | | | |
| | | | .236 | .030 | .007 | .036 |
| 87.5 | 1.875 | .970 | | | | |
| | | | .030 | .003 | .000 | .000 |
| 82.5 | 3.125 | 1.000 | | | | |
| | | | | | .192 | 1.000 |

under the normal curve, we can find the cumulative probability up to the indicated z's. These are shown as $P(Z < z)$. By subtracting the cumulative probabilities at the end-points of the intervals, the probability in each interval is found. For example, $P(Z < .625) = .734$ and $P(Z > −.625) = .266$. Therefore, $P(\bar{x}|\mu_1) = P(−.625 < Z < .625) = .468$. Multiplying $P(\bar{x}|\mu_1)$ by $P(\mu_1)$ from the prior distribution yields the numbers in column six. These products are the successive numerators of Baye's theorem. The denominator is the sum of the numerators and is .192. Dividing each numerator by this sum gives the posterior probabilities in column seven. The posterior distribution is graphed in Figure eight.

The most conspicuous feature of the posterior distribution is the reduction of variability. The prior distribution was represented by seven bars, while the posterior distribution is concentrated in four bars (to three decimal accuracy). Summary statistics, calculated using the midpoints of the intervals, show the change in belief as measured by the prior and posterior distributions:

|  | *Prior* | *Posterior* |
|---|---|---|
| Mean | 101.11 | 98.05 |
| Variance | 21.27 | 10.11 |
| Standard deviation | 4.61 | 3.18 |

The mean of the posterior distribution is less than the mean of the prior, but it is still in the interval centered about 100. Note that even though the sample mean did not fall within this range of values, the bar centered about 100 increased in height! As would be expected, the bar centered about 95 also increased.

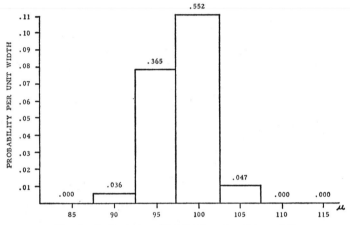

Figure 8. Posterior Distribution for Mean I.Q.

The reduction of variability, as shown by the decrease in the standard deviation, is a measure of the increase in the certainty about $\mu$ after observing the data. This can be illustrated by calculating various posterior probability intervals. For example, combining the two intervals with the greatest probabilities gives $P(92.5 < \mu < 102.5) = .917$. This can be compared with the prior probability interval $P(92.5 < \mu < 107.5) = 900$.

A "classical" .90 confidence interval can be calculated using the methods presented earlier in this chapter.

Lower limit: $95 - 1.65\ (4) = 88.4$
Upper limit: $95 + 1.65\ (4) = 101.6$

The confidence interval is then:

$$C(88.4 < \mu < 101.16) = .90$$

The difference between this interval and the Bayesian posterior interval above arises because the confidence interval uses only the information from the sample, and that information implies the population mean is probably below 100. The Bayesian interval has incorporated that information with the prior belief that $\mu$ may well be above 100. The belief about $\mu$ has shifted down toward the sample mean of 95, but the posterior distribution is still somewhat weighted towards higher values of $\mu$. This illustrates the chain of inference from prior to posterior belief. If more data were collected, the posterior distribution calculated above would become the prior distribution for the next application of Baye's theorem. As more and more data is collected, the posterior distribution tends to converge to the true value of $\mu$. If different people started with different prior distributions, they would tend to have similar posterior distributions after the observation of extensive data.

The reader should be aware that neither the philosophical nor the statistical issues involved in Bayesian statistics have been settled generally. To many, however, Bayesian statistics offer a satisfying way of thinking about statistical inference.

# CHAPTER VI

# Description of Relationships

If a class of ninth-grade algebra students are administered a final examination, a distribution of scores will almost surely result. Since the students were all given the same instruction it might be expected that every student would have learned algebra to the same degree and, therefore, every student would score the same. Why, in fact, do they score differentially? To answer this question, variables must be identified, these having at least one quality. The variables offered as possibilities must be variables which themselves have distributions for this group of students. If all the students scored the same on a certain variable, it could not possibly be influential in explaining why these same students scored differentially on the algebra test.

Numerous variables accounting for differential algebra achievement readily come to mind. For example, "general intelligence," "mathematical aptitude," "motivation," and the like. Other variables, such as "number of days in school," are probably of secondary importance. Variables, such as "hair color," are usually rejected on the basis of irrelevancy, until it is proven otherwise. To research the general question, a decision to investigate "general intelligence" might be made, since it is likely that

TABLE 19

ALGEBRA AND I.Q. SCORES

| Student | I.Q. (X) | Algebra Score (Y) |
|---------|----------|-------------------|
| 1 | 114 | 44 |
| 2 | 106 | 36 |
| 3 | 117 | 35 |
| 4 | 121 | 29 |
| 5 | 112 | 29 |
| 6 | 108 | 25 |
| 7 | 111 | 22 |
| 8 | 115 | 21 |
| 9 | 103 | 21 |
| 10 | 109 | 20 |
| 11 | 105 | 11 |
| 12 | 99 | 7 |

this variable will be quite influential and also because relevant data is usually available. The researcher would record the algebra scores together with the I.Q.'s of each student (making sure that all the I.Q.'s were from the same mental test). In order to illustrate the procedure and yet keep computational work to a minimum, a supposition that there are only twelve students in the class will be made. Their scores are shown in Table 19—with the students ranked according to their algebra scores. A glance at the scores reveals a tendency for the lowest I.Q. scores to be associated with the lowest algebra scores. For example, of the six I.Q.'s below 110, four of them are associated with the four lowest algebra scores. The relation is far from perfect, since the two highest algebra scores are *not* associated with the two highest I.Q. scores. Each student's pair of scores has been plotted as a single point on a X, Y, coordinate axis shown in Figure 9.

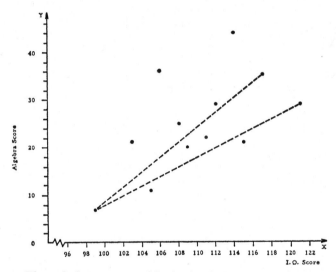

Figure 9. Scattergrams of Student's Algebra and I.Q. Scores

This graph is usually referred to as a scatter diagram, or more simply, a scattergram. A general left to right and low to high pattern can be recognized. (Ignore the two dotted lines at this time.)

In describing relationships, one usually starts with a model. This model, expressed in mathematical terms, is hoped to have two qualities. First, it should adequately represent the data, and second, it should be simple. Unfortunately, these two requisites are not usually harmonious. One could think of drawing a complex curve in Figure 9, which would

connect every point. Starting with (99,7) the curve could proceed to
(103,21) then to (105,11) then to (106,31), etc. Every time the curve
changes from an increasing slope, relative to Y, to a decreasing slope, a
higher power of X is needed in a polynomial equation. The description
of this relationship could be expressed by something looking like

$$Y = a + b_1X + b_2X^2 + b_3X^3 + \ldots + b_8X^8$$

The $b_1, b_2, \ldots, b_8$ are unknown coefficients which could be determined
by a numerical analysis of the data. The "a" in the equation is also unknown and controls the over-all height of the curve relative to Y. Once
we performed the analysis and determined the particular set of numbers,
$a, b_1, b_2, \ldots b_8$, we would have an equation such that if we substituted
any of the I.Q. scores for X, and performed the indicated arithmetic in
the equation, we would obtain a value of Y exactly equal to the algebra
score corresponding to the substituted I.Q. score. This equation, found
by routine curve-fitting techniques, would be a perfect description of our
data! All of the difference (or variability) among the algebra scores
would be completely explained by the differences in the I.Q. scores.

This equation would satisfy the condition that the model adequately
represent the data, but it would be far from a "simple" relationship.
Inherent in its complexity is the probability that the model is not a
general description of the actual relationship between algebra achievement and general intelligence. If more students were tested, we would
be surprised if their points fell exactly on this complex curve. Furthermore, if one of the points were deleted from the graph, say (103,21),
the curve drawn would be quite different from the one described above.
Lastly, since the equation perfectly describes the relationship, there is
nothing "unexplained" meaning that no other variable has anything to
do with algebra achievement.

This leads to the somewhat paradoxical idea that a simpler model
should be set up, one which does not perfectly fit the data at hand. How
simple? In education and psychology, a linear model is usually postulated. Occasionally a model involving a quadratic term, $X^2$, is used, but
a model of cubic or higher degree is extremely rare. Assuming that the
relationship can be described by a straight line, the form of the model,
then, is: $Y = a + bX$. The task is to find the values of "a" and "b" for
this particular set of data.

The problem of determining the two constants, a and b, is not just a
problem in numerical analysis, as it was before. This is because a straight
line does not fit all the points, and, therefore, no unique line exists. The

scattergram reveals that several different lines could be drawn which would appear to be equally "good." For example, one such line would connect the points (99,7) and (121,29), the lower dotted line. Another could be drawn from (97,9) to (118,35), the higher dotted line. This latter line would not go through any of the twelve indicated points, but would appear to offer a "good" representation of the relationship. Two questions arise: (1) how should we conceptualize the model which, in fact, leads to a line which goes through few or no points, and (2) which line among several available should we use?

The answer to the first question is that an error component is added to the model. Suppose the relationship is such that the upper dotted line represents the "true" relationship. By substituting any value of X in the equation for this line, the resulting value of Y is the algebra score which the student would obtain if we measured without error and if no other variables were influential in determining algebra achievement. The equation of the line is $Y = 1.238X - 111.086$. If $X = 103$ is substituted, we obtain $Y = 16.4$. The actual Y score for $X = 103$ is $Y = 21$. To differentiate these two Y values, the value obtained from the equation will be denoted by $Y_e$ (for Y estimated). The error is $Y-Y_e$ or $21-16.4 = 4.6$. This error is thought of as representing measurement error plus all the other variables that we are overlooking. The model becomes: $Y = a + bX + e$ where "e" represents the error component.

It would seem that the values, a and b, should be selected in order to make the errors as small as possible. (Note that in using the complex model all errors were zero.) Some of the errors are positive (actual points above the line) and some are negative (actual points below the line). Rather than merely summing all the errors, the errors are squared before adding to prevent the cancelling effect. An important fact is that the model specifies errors only in the Y scores, not the X scores. Hence, the errors are strictly vertical deviations from the line.

A procedure, known as the method of least squares, is to find a and b such that the sum of squares of all these vertical deviations (errors) is a minimum. Applying the calculus we find that:

$$b = \frac{\sum_{i=1}^{N} (X_i - \bar{X})(Y_i - \bar{Y})}{\sum_{i=1}^{N} (X_i - \bar{X})^2}$$

$$a = \bar{Y} - b\bar{X}$$

The derivation of these formulae will not be shown here, but they are the values which yield the "best" fitting line if "best" is interpreted to mean that the sums of squares of the errors is a minimum.

The quantity in the denominator of the formula for "b" is familiar. It is the sum of squares of deviations of each X score from the mean of the X scores. (The variance of X is this quantity divided by N.) The quantity in the numerator of "b" is the sum of products of the deviations of the Y scores about their mean. (This quantity divided by N is called the *covariance*. It is a measure of how X and Y vary together or "co-vary.") As usual, a computational formula is available. One such formula is

$$b = \frac{\Sigma\,XY - (\Sigma\,X)\,(\Sigma\,Y)/N}{\Sigma\,X^2 - (\Sigma\,X)^2/N}$$

TABLE 20

|  | X | Y | X² | Y² | XY |
|---|---|---|---|---|---|
|  | 114 | 44 | 12996 | 1936 | 5016 |
|  | 106 | 36 | 11236 | 1296 | 3816 |
|  | 117 | 35 | 13689 | 1225 | 4095 |
|  | 121 | 29 | 14641 | 841 | 3509 |
|  | 112 | 29 | 12544 | 841 | 3248 |
|  | 108 | 25 | 11664 | 625 | 2700 |
|  | 111 | 22 | 12321 | 484 | 2442 |
|  | 115 | 21 | 13225 | 441 | 2415 |
|  | 103 | 21 | 10609 | 441 | 2163 |
|  | 109 | 20 | 11881 | 400 | 2180 |
|  | 105 | 11 | 11025 | 121 | 1155 |
|  | 99 | 7 | 9801 | 49 | 693 |
| *Totals* | 1320 | 300 | 145632 | 8700 | 33432 |

The quantities necessary to calculate "b" are shown in Table 20. Short-cut procedures utilizing computation variables are available but these will not be shown. Substituting in the formulae for "a" and "b" yields:

$$b = \frac{33432 - (1320)\,(300)/12}{145632 - (1320)^2/12}$$

$$b = \frac{33432 - 33000}{145632 - 145200}$$

$$b = 1$$

$$a = 300/12 - (1)\,(1320/12)$$

$$a = 25 - 110$$

$$a = -85$$

The best fitting line is:

$$Y_e = -85 + X$$

which is graphed in Figure 10.

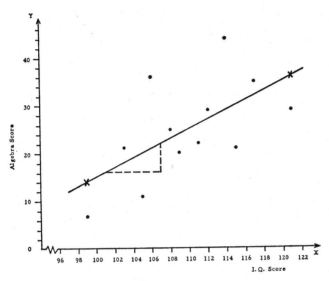

Figure 10. Best Fitting Line

Two features of this line should be noted. First, the line has a slope of one. That is, the change in Y per unit change in X is one. To verify this, note that the line goes through (100,15) and (104,19). As X changed 4 units to the right, Y changed 4 units upward. Therefore, the slope is $4/4 = 1$. The dotted lines in Figure 10 show the change in Y as X changes. Visually, it appears that the slope is 1/2, but note that the Y and X axes are scaled in the ratio 2/1. The slope of the line is equal to "b," which is called the regression coefficient. The line itself is called the regression line of Y on X. The second feature of interest is that the regression line goes through the point $(\bar{X},\bar{Y})$. In this case $\bar{X} = 110$ and $\bar{Y} = 25$. The reader can verify the assertion.

The regression line is a description of the relationship between algebra achievement and general intelligence, but it does not indicate the magnitude of the relationship. Figure 11 shows three scattergrams, each having the same regression line as found above, but each having a different magnitude of relationship between X and Y.

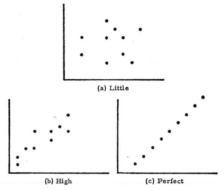

(a) Little

(b) High          (c) Perfect

Figure 11. Scattergrams Displaying Different Amounts of Relationship

Scattergram (a) shows almost no relationship between X and Y. Scattergram (b) is an example of a high relationship. The majority of the points are close to the regression line while scattergram (c) shows a perfect relationship. All the points are on the line. The "closeness" of the actual points to the regression line is a measure of the strength of the relationship. The problem of quantifying the amount of "closeness" results in a neat solution.

Recall that the original motivation for this whole problem was to explain why the students scored differentially on the algebra test. The usual measure of the amount of difference or variability is the variance (or standard deviation). Consequently, one is motivated to search for a relationship between the variance of the Y scores, $S_y^2$, and the errors. This is accomplished as follows:

Start with the identity:

$$Y - \bar{Y} = Y - \bar{Y}$$

Subtract and add $Y_e$:

$$Y - \bar{Y} = Y - Y_e + Y_e - \bar{Y}$$

Group:

$$Y - \bar{Y} = (Y - Y_e) + (Y_e - \bar{Y})$$

Since the errors are $e = Y - Y_e$:

$$Y - \bar{Y} = e + (Y_e - \bar{Y})$$

Square both sides:

$$(Y - \bar{Y})^2 = [e + (Y - \bar{Y})]^2$$
$$(Y - \bar{Y})^2 = e^2 + (Y - \bar{Y})^2 + 2e(Y - \bar{Y})$$

Sum over N observations on both sides:

$$\Sigma(Y - Y)^2 = \Sigma e^2 + \Sigma(Y - \bar{Y})^2 + \Sigma 2e(Y - \bar{Y})$$

The last term on the right side can be shown to be identically zero. Therefore,

$$\Sigma(Y - \bar{Y})^2 = \Sigma e^2 + \Sigma(Y - \bar{Y})^2$$

Divide both sides by N:

$$\frac{\Sigma(Y - \bar{Y})^2}{N} = \frac{\Sigma e^2}{N} + \frac{\Sigma(Y_e - \bar{Y})^2}{N}$$

The term on the left side is the variance of Y, $S_y^2$. The variance of the errors is $\Sigma(e-\bar{e})^2/N$, but it happens that the mean of the errors about the regression line is always zero. Hence, the variance of the errors, $S_e^2$ is $\Sigma e^2/N$. It is also true that the mean of the estimated Y's is the same as the mean of the observed Y's. Consequently, the variance of the estimated Y scores, $S_{ye}^2$, is $\Sigma(Y_e - \bar{Y})^2/N$. The last identity above can then be written as:

$$S_y^2 = S_e^2 + S_{ye}^2$$

which says that the variance of the actual Y scores can be decomposed into two additive parts. The first part is the variance of the errors and the second part is the variance of the estimated Y scores.

Since the mean of the errors is zero, the variance of the errors can be thought of as not only a measure of the dispersion of the errors, but also as a measure of their magnitude. For example, suppose there are four errors: 5, 3, −3, −5. Then, $S_e^2 = (25 + 9 + 9 + 25)/4 = 68/4 = 17$. If the errors increase, they must increase both in the positive and negative directions since they must remain "anchored" at zero. For example, 7, 4, −2, −9. The errors still add to zero, but $S_e^2 = (49 + 16 + 4 + 81)/4 = 150/4 = 37.5$. The variance of the errors has increased. The measure of "closeness" of the points to the regression line is, then, $S_e^2$.

The net result is that one can conceptualize the problem of relationship in the following way. We desired to "explain" the variability in the algebra scores. We chose a variable, I.Q., which we hoped would account for this variability. We used a "best-fitting" line, which yields an estimated algebra score, $Y_e$, (or "predicted" algebra score) for each student on the basis of his I.Q. score. We could possibly make errors in our estimation or prediction, and a measure of the magnitude of these errors is given by $S_e^2$. If these errors are large, we would observe a large $S_e^2$ and the amount of variance due to the regression of Y on X would be small. Our "explanation" of $S_y^2$ would be poor. On the other hand if the errors are small, then $S_e^2$ is small and the amount of variance due to the regression of Y on X is large. Our "explanation" of $S_y^2$ would then be good.

Scattergram (c) in Figure 11 shows a perfect relationship between Y and X. Since all the points are on the line, the errors are zero or $S_e^2 = 0$. Then,

$$S_y^2 = 0 + S_{ye}^2 = S_{ye}^2$$

All of the variance in the Y scores is due to the regression of Y on X. If there is no relationship between Y and X, then $S_{ye}^2 = 0$ and

$$S_y^2 = S_e^2 + 0 = S_e^2$$

None of the variance in the Y scores is due to the regression of Y and X. All of the variance of Y is "unexplained."

Table 21 shows the estimated scores and the errors for the algebra

TABLE 21

ESTIMATED ALGEBRA SCORES AND ERRORS

| X | Y | $Y_e$ | $Y - Y_e = e$ |
|---|---|---|---|
| 114 | 44 | 29 | 15 |
| 106 | 36 | 21 | 15 |
| 117 | 35 | 32 | 3 |
| 121 | 29 | 36 | −7 |
| 112 | 29 | 27 | 2 |
| 108 | 25 | 23 | 2 |
| 111 | 22 | 26 | −4 |
| 115 | 21 | 30 | −9 |
| 103 | 21 | 18 | 3 |
| 109 | 20 | 24 | −4 |
| 105 | 11 | 20 | −9 |
| 99 | 7 | 14 | −7 |
| | 300 | 300 | 0 |

$$\Sigma Y_e^2 = 7932 \qquad S_{ye} = 7932/12 - (300/12)^2 = 36$$
$$\Sigma e^2 = 768 \qquad S_e^2 = 768/12 \qquad\qquad\quad = 64$$
$$\Sigma Y^2 = 8700 \qquad S_y^2 = 8700/12 - (300/12)^2 = 100$$

problem. The estimated scores are found by substituting each X score in the regression equation $Y_e = -85 + X$. Note that the actual Y scores and estimated Y scores both add to 300 which verifies that $\bar{Y} = \bar{Y}_e$. Also, the errors sum to zero which verifies that $\bar{e} = 0$. The sums of squares of the errors and the sums of the squares of the predicted Y scores add to the sums of squares of the actual Y scores. The variances are found using the usual computational formula and are:

$$S_e^2 = 64$$
$$\underline{S_{ye}^2 = 36}$$
$$S_y^2 = 100$$

This result verifies the additivity of the variances.

For a given $S_e^2$, the size of $S_e^2$, or equivalently, the size of $S_{ye}^2$, is indicative of the amount of relationship between X and Y. Since $S_y^2$ can change from problem to problem, the statistic which is adopted to indicate the amount of relationship must incorporate $S_y^2$ and either $S_{ye}^2$ or $S_e^2$. A commonly used statistic, which does just that, is denoted by $r^2$ and is defined to be:

$$r^2 = S_{ye}^2/S_y^2$$

If the relationship is perfect, then $S_y^2 = S_{ye}^2$. Then, the statistic, $r^2$, is unity. If there is no relationship, $S_{ye}^2 = 0$. Then, $r^2$ is zero. The minimum value of $r^2$ is zero, indicating no relationship, and the maximum value is unity, indicating perfect relationship. The usual situation in practice is to find $r^2$ taking on some intermediate value.

For the algebra problem:

$$r^2 = 36/100 = .36$$

This would be interpreted to mean that thirty-six percent of the total variance of Y is attributable to the regression of Y on X (or sixty-four percent is still "unexplained").

The square root of $r^2$ is known as the Pearson product-moment correlation coefficient, r. In the algebra problem, $r^2 = .36$ so r is either $+.6$ or $-.6$ since squaring either a positive or a negative number would result in a positive $r^2$. The sign of r is determined by the slope of the regression line. The line found above had a slope of one ($b = 1$). Since the slope is positive, the sign of r is positive or $r = +.6$. If the slope were negative the line would incline from the upper left to the lower right, and the sign of r would be negative. A negative correlation coefficient would mean that high values of Y are associated with low values of X, while low values of Y are associated with high values of X. A positive correlation coefficient would mean that high values of Y are associated with high values of X and low Y values associated with low X values. Since $0 \leq r^2 \leq +1$, then $-1 \leq r \leq +1$.

If r is either $-1$ or $+1$, the relationship is perfect since in both cases $r^2 = +1$. If $r = 0$, there is no relationship since $r^2 = 0$. Most often, it is the statistic, r, that is reported in research articles, books, etc. One can interpret the reported value by squaring it and thinking in terms of proportion of variance due to the regression of Y on X. Calculation formulae also exist for r so that one would not need to go through the complete regression procedure. These will not be shown, however.

The sixty-four percent of the variance due to error in the algebra problem might be further reduced by adding another variable such as "mathematical aptitude," W, to the model. The model becomes:

$$Y = a + bX + cW + e$$

One could minimize the sums of squares of the errors in this model and derive solutions for a, b and c. As before, estimated Y scores could be calculated and the ratio of the variance of the estimated scores to the total variance of the actual scores would give a measure of relationship, which is denoted by $R^2$. In this case, the model is called a multiple regression model and the square root of $R^2$ equal to R is called the multiple correlation coefficient. Essentially, no new ideas enter, except that the arithmetic becomes more complicated. Computer programs are available which are able to handle up to thirty or more variables. The computer output usually lists the regression coefficients and the multiple correlation coefficient, R. The output also frequently lists all possible simple correlation coefficients between the variables. One is able to see what proportion of variance is attributable to the regression of Y on each variable used alone by scanning the $r^2$'s and what proportion of variance is attributable to the regression of Y on all the variables together by inspecting $R^2$.

Prediction is generally far from perfect, but, variables, such as high-school rank, I.Q. and, college board scores, can account for up to eighty percent of the variance in college grade-point averages. This information can be of great value to a high-school counsellor in predicting future academic success.

As one might expect, there is a functional relationship between the correlation coefficient, r, and the regression coefficient, b. It is

$$b = rS_y/S_x$$

If the standard deviation for Y and X are equal, then b = r. If the raw scores are converted to standard scores, $z_y$ and $z_x$, a simple representation of the regression line is obtained. Since standard scores have equal standard deviations (each equal to unity), the regression coefficient will be r, the correlation coefficient. In addition, since the means of the standard scores are both zero, the "a" in the equation must be zero. Hence,

$$z_{ye} = rz_x$$

The estimated z score for Y is the z score for X multiplied by the correlation coefficient.

An interesting fact is apparent from the equation written in this form. Since $-1 \leq r \leq 1$, the estimated $z_{ye}$ can never be larger, in absolute value, than $z_x$. For the algebra problem, r = .6, so

$$z_{ye} = .6\,z_x$$

A student having a standard score of $+1$ on X (one standard deviation above the X mean) has an estimated standard score of .6 on Y (six-tenths standard deviations above the Y mean). Similarly, if $z_x = -2$, then $z_{ye} = -1.2$. That is, a student, who is two standard deviations below the mean of X, has an estimated Y score of only 1.2 standard deviations below the Y mean. It is because of this fact that the term, regression, is used. Predicted Y scores are said to have "regressed" towards the Y mean. If $r = +1$ or $-1$ (perfect positive or negative correlation), then there is no regression effect since $z_{ye} = z_x$, respectively.

Data on heights of fathers and their sons is reported by Frederick Mosteller et al.[1] Regarding the son's height as the Y variable and the father's height as the X variable, the regression equation in standard form, is reported as:

$$z_{ye} = .51\,z_x$$

Note that r = .51. A father who is considered tall, say two standard deviations above the mean of the fathers' heights, would be estimated to have a "shorter" son, in the sense that, relative to the mean of the sons' heights, the singular would only be 1.02 standard deviations above that mean. Similarly, a father who is considered short, say two standard deviations below the mean of the fathers' heights, would have a son who would be estimated to be "taller," in the sense that the son would be only 1.02 standard deviations below the mean of the sons' heights. This regression effect has been interpreted by some to mean that eventually all will be the same height. If sons' heights are predicted to be

---

[1] Frederick Mosteller, et al., Probability with Statistical Applications, (Massachusetts: Addison-Wesley, 1961), p. 394. Data was collected by Karl Pearson and Alice Lee.

closer to their mean and, in turn, their sons closer to their mean, the above statement seems reasonable. Inspection of the data, however, contradicts this assertion. The means and standard deviations are (in inches):

|  | Sons | Fathers |
|---|---|---|
| Means | 68.66 | 64.70 |
| Standard deviations | 2.74 | 2.73 |

The mean height of the sons is higher than the mean of the fathers, but the important fact to notice is that the standard deviation of the sons' heights is *not* smaller than the standard deviation of the fathers' heights. The sons are as variable as the fathers in terms of heights! They are not "closer" to their mean than their fathers were to their mean.

This example shows that even though *predicted* y values regress towards the y mean that the *actual* y values are not necessarily less (or more) variable around the y mean than the x values are around the x mean. To examine the regression effect in more detail some fictitious data is shown in Table 22.[2]

TABLE 22

ILLUSTRATION OF REGRESSION EFFECT

| Post-Test Scores (Y) | Post-Test Means | | | | | | |
|---|---|---|---|---|---|---|---|
|  | 11.5 | 12 | 12.5 | 13 | 13.5 | 14 | 14.5 |
| 16 |  |  |  | 1 | 1 | 1 | 1 |
| 15 |  |  | 1 | 1 | 2 | 1 | 1 |
| 14 |  | 1 | 2 | 3 | 3 | 2 | 1 |
| 13 | 1 | 1 | 3 | 4 | 3 | 1 | 1 |
| 12 | 1 | 2 | 3 | 3 | 2 | 1 |  |
| 11 | 1 | 1 | 2 | 1 | 1 |  |  |
| 10 | 1 | 1 | 1 | 1 |  |  |  |
|  | 7 | 8 | 9 | 10 | 11 | 12 | 13 |

Pre-Test Scores (x)

The data show the results of two administrations of the same test to a group of fifty-eight students. The numbers in the body of the table indicate the numbers of students scoring various combinations of x and y. For example, four students scored 10 on the pre-test and 13 on the post-test. From the symmetry of the table, it can be seen that the pre-test mean, x̄, is 10 and the post-test mean is ȳ = 13. In addition, the amount of variability around x is equal to the amount of variability

---

[2] Data, slightly modified, from Campbell, D. and Stanley, J. "Experimental and Quasi-Experimental Designs for Research on Teaching" in *Handbook of Research on Teaching,* (Chicago: Rand McNally and Co., 1963).

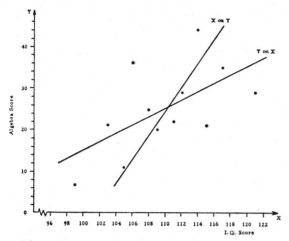

Figure 12. Regression Lines for Algebra Problem

around $\bar{y}$. Even though $\bar{y}$ is larger than $\bar{x}$, the standard deviations, $S_x$ and $S_y$, are equal. The correlation coefficient for this data is $r = .50$, so the regression line for predicting y from x, in standard form, is:

$$z_{ye} = .50 \, z_x$$

The regression effect is illustrated by the post-test means for the students scoring various values of x. The four students who scored 7 on the pre-test averaged 11.5 on the post-test. The six students scoring 8 on the pre-test average 12 on the post-test, etc. The important point is that the regression line for predicting y from x is the line that connects these means. Consequently, it is these sub-class means that are the predicted values, $y_e$. The x values ranged from 7 to 13, but the predicted values range from 11.5 to 14.5. Those students who were three points above $\bar{x}$ at $x = 13$ have a predicted score of 14.5, which is only 1.5 points above $\bar{y}$. Similarly, those students scoring $x = 8$ were two points below $\bar{x}$, but their predicted value is 12 which is only one point below $\bar{y}$.

This regression of sub-class means is not just a statistical artifact. It has been observed in many sets of actual data. In the height example, discussed earlier, it is an actual fact that fathers of a particular height have sons whose *average* height is closer to the over-all height of sons than the particular fathers' height was to the over-all mean height of fathers.

It is important in educational experimentation that the regression effect be understood and dealt with effectively. Campbell and Stanley[3]

---

[3] *Ibid.*, p. 180–182.

discuss several examples of regression effect. Here is one. Suppose that the increase in the over-all mean test score for the data in Table 22 represents "practice effect" on the test, but otherwise the reason for the imperfect correlation is a result of errors of measurement. If we test a group of children and then select those who score 7 and 8 for remedial work, we can predict almost certainly that, even if the remedial work has no effect, these children will show greater relative improvement, on the average, than other children in this class. Initially, the students who scored 7 were three points below $\bar{x}$, but later are only 1.5 points below the class mean. The students who were two points above $\bar{x}$ are later only one point above the class mean. If this happened, one can appreciate how it might be concluded that the remedial work is really worthwhile. Actually it may be worthless, since this result may only be the effect of regression.

In the previous examples, the y variable was the variable to be predicted, while the x variable was the variable used for the prediction. It is reasonable to think of algebra achievement as a function of I.Q. or sons' heights as a function of fathers' heights. This is not to imply that x causes y, but there is a natural order (in time, at least) of these variables. There is no reason, however, why one could not investigate the estimated I.Q. score for students with a particular algebra achievement or the estimated father's height given knowledge of the son's height. There may be little motivation to do so, but one could proceed exactly as before, except that the x variable would be interchanged with the y variable. In addition, there are numerous examples of bi-variate data where there is no natural order between the variables—such as standing height and arm length or algebra achievement and social studies achievement. Either one of the variables could be thought of as the y variable. For these examples, one is interested primarily in how these variables co-vary or are related.

For any given set of data involving two variables, if the x variable is interchanged with the y variable, another regression line can be derived. This line would be the regression line for predicting x from y. It is not the same line as the line of regression for predicting y from x. The formula for the x on y line is the same as the y on x line except that x and y are interchanged. Consequently,

$$z_{x_e} = r z_y$$

Solving for $z_y$ yields

$$z_y = \frac{1}{r} z_{x_e}$$

This shows that, if y is plotted on the vertical axis, then the slope of the line for predicting x from y is $1/r$. Since r can never be larger than one (in absolute value), the slope is a number greater than or equal to one (in absolute value), since dividing unity by a fraction results in a number larger than unity. If both regression lines are plotted on the same scattergram with y as the vertical axis, the x on y line will have the larger slope (in absolute value). Figure 12 shows the regression line for estimating I.Q. from knowledge of the algebra score (x on y) together with the y on x line derived previously. Both lines go through $(\bar{x}, \bar{y})$ which is the intersection point.

The common element of the two lines is the correlation coefficient, r. The proportion of variance attributable to the regression of y on x is the same as the proportion of variance attributable to the regression of x on y, i.e.

$$S^2_{ye}/S^2_y = S^2_{xe}/S^2_x = r^2$$

This means that $r^2$ or r is a measure of the linear relationship of x and y, regardless of which variable is thought of as the "predictor" and which variable is "predicted."

It is interesting to note that, since there are two regression lines, the regression effect operates in both directions. That is, the x means for given y scores are closer to the over-all mean of x than the original y scores are to the y mean, in addition to the effect discussed previously. If $r = 1$, then the two regression lines coincide. In this case, there is no regression effect in either direction since $z_{ye} = z_x$ and $z_{xe} = z_y$.

Oftentimes, the correlation coefficient is calculated directly without deriving the regression lines. The following list is presented to give the reader an idea of the magnitude of correlation coefficients actually found in educational and psychological studies.

| Variable 1 | Variable 2 | r |
|---|---|---|
| I.Q. scores | English achievement (high school) | .74 |
| I.Q. scores | Trigonometry achievement (high school) | .34 |
| Verbal I.Q. | Performance I.Q. (at age 10.5) | .68 |
| Height | arm spread | .80 |
| Age (below 20 years) | I.Q. | .00 |
| Scholastic-aptitude scores | hours of study | −.70 |

(for college students with the same grade-point average)

The fact that I.Q. and age are *not* correlated is one reason why I.Q. is a popular measure. If there were a consistent trend between these variables, one would need a table of ages and I.Q.'s in order to properly interpret I.Q. The negative correlation of "hours of study" and scholastic-aptitude scores is likely to be surprising, but note that this is for students who have actually achieved equally well. It means that the "brighter" students do not study as long as the "not so bright" students to achieve the same grade-point average.

One of the most common errors made in interpreting correlation coefficients is to imply a causal mechanism between variables which are correlated. If one considers average salary of teachers measured in various years and consumption of alcohol in the United States for those same years, a fairly high correlation is obtained. Does this imply a cause and effect relationship? In other words, does more money in teachers' pockets mean that the consumption of alcohol will necessarily increase in the United States? Perhaps, the reverse is true. When consumption of alcohol increases, teachers get salary increases since the school board members, while under the influence of alcohol, feel more liberal with the district's money. The true explanation is probably neither of these. Perhaps a general "prosperity" variable is related to both teachers' salaries and consumption of alcohol. A relationship does not imply a causal mechanism! Does intelligence "cause" algebra achievement? Certainly these two variables are related, but to imply cause and effect is to infer further than the data permit. The relationship between the number of cigarettes smoked per day and the incidence of lung cancer is another example. No one doubts the relationship. What has been argued for many years is whether the infusion of cigarette smoke into the lungs is a mechanism which causes the formation of cancerous tissue. It may, indeed, be a cause, but this conclusion is not valid merely on the basis of an observed relationship.

# Bibliography

*Elementary*

Blommers, Paul, and E. F. Lindquist, *Elementary Statistical Methods in Psychology and Education.* Boston: Houghton Mifflin Company, 1960.

Clarke, Robert B., Arthur P. Coladari, and John Caffrey, *Statistical Reasoning and Procedures.* Columbus, Ohio: Charles E. Merrill, Inc., 1965.

Downie, N. M., and R. W. Heath, *Basic Statistical Methods.* New York: Harper & Row, Publishers, 1959.

Ferguson, George A., *Statistical Analysis in Psychology and Education.* Second Edition. New York: McGraw-Hill Book Company, 1966.

Gourevitch, Vivian, *Statistical Methods: A Problem-Solving Approach.* Boston: Allyn and Bacon, Inc., 1965.

Guilford, J. P., *Fundamental Statistics in Psychology and Education.* New York: McGraw-Hill Book Company, 1956.

Hammond, Kenneth R., and James E. Householder, *Introduction to the Statistical Method.* New York: Alfred A. Knopf, 1962.

McCarthy, Philip J., *Introduction to Statistical Reasoning.* New York: McGraw-Hill Book Company, 1957.

McCollough, Celeste, and Toche Van Atta, *Statistical Concepts.* New York: McGraw-Hill Book Company, 1963.

McNemar, Quinn, *Psychological Statistics.* New York: John Wiley and Sons, Inc., 1962.

Wallis, W. A., and H. V. Roberts, *Statistics: A New Approach.* New York: Free Press, 1957.

*Advanced*

Dixon, W., and F. Massey, *Introduction to Statistical Analysis.* Second Edition. New York: McGraw-Hill Book Company, 1957.

Edwards, Allen L., *Experimental Design in Psychological Research.* Revised Edition. New York: Holt, Rinehart and Winston, Inc., 1960.

Fisher, Ronald A., *The Design of Experiments.* Third Edition. Edinburgh: Oliver and Boyd, 1942.

Hays, William L., *Statistics for Psychologists.* New York: Holt, Rinehart and Winston, Inc., 1963.

Huntsberger, David V., *Elements of Statistical Inference.* Boston: Allyn and Bacon, Inc., 1961.

Johnson, Palmer O., and Robert W. B. Jackson, *Modern Statistical Methods: Descriptive and Inductive.* Chicago: Rand McNally and Company, 1959.

111

Lindley, D. V., *Introduction to Probability and Statistics from a Bayesian Viewpoint*. Cambridge: Cambridge University Press, 1965.

Lindquist, E. F., *Design and Analysis of Experiments in Psychology and Education*. Boston: Houghton Mifflin Company, 1953.

Snedecor, George W., *Statistical Methods*. Fifth Edition. Ames, Iowa: Iowa State College Press, 1956.

Tate, Merle W., *Statistics in Education and Psychology*. New York: The Macmillan Company, 1965.

Winer, B. J., *Statistical Principles in Experimental Design*. New York: McGraw-Hill Book Company, 1962.

*Index*

# *Index*